The Ivory Sundials of Nuremberg

The Ivory Sundials of Nuremberg
1500–1700

Penelope Gouk

Published in conjunction with an exhibition of dials from the Museum of the History of Science, Oxford, and the Whipple Museum of the History of Science, Cambridge, arranged by the Whipple Museum

Cambridge, 1988

For Nigel

Published by the Whipple Museum of the History of Science, Free School Lane, Cambridge CB2 3RH, UK.

Research and Editorial Assistant: Hubert M. Stadler

British Library Cataloguing in Publication Data
Gouk, Penelope
    The Ivory Sundials of Nuremberg 1500–1700
    1. Nuremberg sundials
    I. Title
    529'.78

    ISBN 0 906271 03 7

Photographs of exhibited diptychs: Don Manning
Line Drawings: Joanna Cameron
Design and Lay-out: Colin Davies
Set, printed and bound in Great Britain by Eyre & Spottiswoode Ltd, London & Margate

CONTENTS

LIST OF TABLES AND PLATES

Abbreviations used throughout

BL = London, British Library
BM = London, British Museum
RAS = London, Royal Astronomical Society
BNM = Munich, Bayerisches Nationalmuseum
BSB = Munich, Bayerische Staatsbibliothek
GNM = Nuremberg, Germanisches Nationalmuseum
NSA = Nuremberg, Stadtarchiv

Preface

Ivory sundials made in Nuremberg during the sixteenth and seventeenth centuries are found in museums and private collections world-wide. Portable, compact, attractively decorated and relatively durable, the Nuremberg diptychs have always found a ready international market. Apart from their purely aesthetic attraction these instruments are also of technical and scientific interest as they represent some of the most up-to-date technology of the period.

This book offers the first comprehensive and inter-disciplinary study of the Nuremberg ivory diptychs and the cultural context in which they were manufactured and marketed. It is divided into two main parts. In the first section, a series of basic questions which might be asked about the instruments by any interested non-specialist is taken as the starting-point for enquiry. Drawing on archival material, published texts, data from new scientific analysis and contemporary illustrations, I have considered the diptychs from a number of viewpoints, making use of the methods of as many different disciplines as possible. By means of this multi-disciplinary approach, I have attempted to build up a composite picture of the instruments, the makers and their milieu. The structure and function of the diptychs as scientific instruments and decorative objects, the materials and tools used for their manufacture, the social and economic conditions which gave rise to their production and distribution are all equally important parts of the story. The second section of the book consists of a catalogue of the exhibition 'The Ivory Sundials of Nuremberg, 1500–1700' which has been organized in conjunction with this publication by the Whipple Museum of the History of Science, Cambridge. The exhibition is based on instruments from the Museum of the History of Science, Oxford, and the Whipple Museum, Cambridge. All the diptychs in the exhibition are illustrated here with photographs by Don Manning. Since I have used these as the basis for my observations about technical and ornamental aspects of the instruments in the first part of the book, the photographs are not confined to the catalogue section but are distributed throughout the text. The catalogue number is found in the caption to each figure or Plate, and the numbers of these are listed in the catalogue entries. The principal makers' marks and stylistic features of the diptychs are also illustrated and identified in the catalogue section.

There are many individuals who have contributed to the remaining illustrations. Joanna Cameron produced all the line drawings and maps which Barry Brown helped me to design. Thanks are given to all the institutions which have given permission for their objects to be reproduced here, and to all those who have supplied photographs. The sources of these are individually acknowledged in the List of Plates and the captions to the figures.

In writing this book I have been helped by more people than it is possible to mention. I would like to thank the directors and staff of all the museums and libraries whose collections I have used for this study. These include the Ashmolean Museum, Oxford; the Bayerische Nationalmuseum and Bayerische Staatsbibliothek, Munich; the Bayerische Staatsarchiv Nuremberg; the Bodleian Library, Oxford; the British Library and the British Museum, London; the Deutsche Museum, Munich; the Germanische Nationalmuseum, Nuremberg; the Landeskirchliche Archiv, Nuremberg; the Museo Poldi-Pezzoli, Milan; the Museum of the History of Science, Oxford; the Museum of London; the Royal Astronomical Society, the Royal Society and the Science Museum, London; the Stadtarchiv and Stadtbibliothek as well as the Stadtgeschichtlichen Museen, Nuremberg; the Victoria and Albert Museum, London; the Warburg Institute, University of London, and the Whipple Museum of the History of Science, Cambridge.

The technical information and research provided by Barbara Boehm, Martin Biddle, Ian Bostridge, Barry Brown, Michael Crawforth, Hazel Forsythe, Hermann Froschauer, Willem Hackmann, Julian Henderson, Katy Kelly, J. Rolf Mauersberger, Catherine Mortimer and Margaret Rule is gratefully acknowledged. Ruth Neumann provided the preliminary translation of the three available versions of the rules of the compass-makers' craft. The *Compass-Makers' Statute* (Table 7) was produced by Hubert Stadler based on these drafts. He also provided the German summary on pages 113–4.

I thank everyone who has given me help, encouragement, constructive criticism and advice at the various stages in the production of this work. Apart from those people already mentioned, these include Albert Bartelmess, Jim Bennett, David Bryden, Peter Hingley, Arthur MacGregor, Francis Maddison, Klaus Maurice, Lorenz Seelig, Anthony Simcock, Michael Snodin, Hubert Stadler, David Thompson, Anthony Turner, Gerard L'E. Turner, Roderick and Marjorie Webster, Johannes Willers and Michael Wright. My research was completed and the book written during the first part of a three-year British Academy post-doctoral Research Fellowship held at the University of Oxford from October 1986.

P.M.G.
May 1988

CHAPTER ONE

What are they and how do they work?

Sundials tell time by means of the shadow cast by an indicator, or gnomon, on to a surface marked with hour lines, known as the dial plate. *Gnōmōn* is the Greek word for 'one who shows'. Sundials are either fixed, such as those found on walls and in gardens, or portable. Since the Nuremberg ivory sundials are portable, as are all the sundials referred to here, the fixed group can be conveniently omitted from the following classification (based on Higgins I; Michel I, 28–33; Turner, 174).

The shadow cast by the sun changes in both length and direction as the sun appears to move from east to west in the course of the day (fig. 1). Sundials can therefore use the sun in two different ways. The *altitude dial* marks the sun's changing angular distance above the horizon (altitude). The *shepherd* or *pillar dial* is an example of this form of sundial; its use in Europe dates from before 1100 (fig. 2).

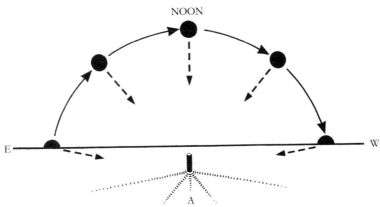

1 The shadow cast by the sun
To the observer at A, looking south, the sun appears to rise in the east, reaching its maximum height at noon, and to set in the west. The shadow of the gnomon cast by the sun thus continuously changes in both length and direction in the course of the day. (The explanation here and those throughout refer to the northern hemisphere only.)

The *direction dial* relies on the sun's changing direction in the sky. Here the gnomon is normally aligned with the earth's polar axis, and it is the *angle* of its shadow which indicates the hour. Most direction dials, including the Nuremberg sundials, are hour-angle dials, but some measure the sun's angular distance along the horizon (azimuth) and are known as azimuth dials. Since these were not made in Nuremberg, they need not be discussed here in any further detail. All direction dials must be properly aligned in order to work correctly, and it is for this reason that portable ones are usually provided with small magnetic compasses.

Exactly when a magnetic compass was first added to a sundial has not yet been firmly established, although it is likely to have been early in the fifteenth century (Turner, 26). The combination of sundial and compass in portable form was already known as a 'compass' (*Kompasz*) in the 1480s in Nuremberg, and the term passed into popular usage among authors such as Johann Schöner, Peter Apian and Sebastian Munster (H. Wagner, 179–82). By the early decades of the sixteenth century the 'compass-maker', working in ivory, brass and wood, had become a recognized specialist craftsman in the city. Other places were soon to exploit the

2 Pillar dial in boxwood;
Nuremberg, c. 1470/80
BNM, Inv. no. 76/152.

obvious demand for such instruments. During the sixteenth and seventeenth centuries, portable sundials of many varieties were produced in great numbers in manufacturing centres throughout Europe (Drecker; Higgins II; Körber; Zinner I). Apart from Nuremberg, Augsburg was the other main south German town with an organized trade of compass-making. The Augsburg sundials, however, were usually made of brass, not ivory (Bobinger). The only other centre where ivory sundials were produced in any great quantity in the seventeenth century was Dieppe (see Chapter two).

In this exhibition attention is focused on one special group of portable ivory sundials produced in Nuremberg between about 1500 and 1700. These are made of two leaves or tablets hinged together so that when they are opened out they form a right angle to each other. It is for this reason that they are usually called *diptych dials* or *tablet dials* (*Klapp-Sonnenuhren* in modern German).

Strictly speaking, the Nuremberg diptych is not a single dial, but is a form of multiple dial, consisting of several dial plates. These almost always include a horizontal dial on the inside of the lower leaf and a vertical dial on the inside upper leaf. A single string serves as the gnomon for both. Because it has to be aligned with the earth's polar axis, the string-gnomon is sometimes referred to as the *pole-string*. The magnetic compass is always recessed into the lower leaf of the diptych.

In addition to the basic string-gnomon dials, the Nuremberg diptych usually has several small dial plates, each of which has a pin-gnomon (see fig. 16). When the dial plate is in the form of a shallow hollow it is known as a *scaphe*. As will be explained more fully below, some of the pin-gnomon dials on the diptychs are altitude dials.

The compass-makers of Nuremberg apparently did not limit themselves to the production of ivory diptych dials, even though most instruments which survive today are of this type. Some diptych dials, for example, were made of wood or brass. Another form of 'compass' they made was the horizontal dial with compass, usually in the shape of a small round box. Other ingenious compass dials, in the form of a crucifix, cube or polyhedron, for example, were also occasionally produced, but these will not be considered in the present study (e.g. Ward, 32–3). When the term 'Nuremberg ivory sundial' is used here, it can thus be understood as referring to the diptych. (For the single exception to this rule, an ivory pillar dial of 1455, see below, fig. 26.)

The changing position of the sun

The sun's observed altitude and its path between sunrise and sunset in any particular location vary not only according to the time of day, but also according to the season of the year. The *declination* of the sun, its angular distance north or south of the equator, changes from day to day as the sun apparently completes its yearly path through the heavens, which is known as the *ecliptic*. The ecliptic is inclined to the plane of the equator at an angle of approximately $23\frac{1}{2}°$.

This account of the sun's motions is based on the concepts of the geocentric Ptolemaic system, which was becoming superseded by the heliocentric Copernican system in the period covered by this book. Yet the notion that the earth was at the centre of the universe served as a means of description for everyday observations perfectly well, and continued to be used by makers and users of such instruments.

It is, of course, the earth which moves; it rotates anti-clockwise about its axis once every twenty-four hours at the same time as it moves anti-clockwise around the sun, taking a year (approximately $365\frac{1}{4}$ days) to complete its circuit. The earth's axis is not perpendicular to the plane of its rotation but departs from the vertical by an angle of about $23\frac{1}{2}°$ and points towards the celestial North pole, conveniently marked by a fairly bright star called the Pole star. It is the earth's tilt which is responsible for the changing seasons and day length.

In fact the earth's axis does not remain completely steady as it rotates, but describes a small circle once every 26,000 years. This 'wobbling' motion results in a movement of the celestial pole, which is usually displaced from the Pole star by a few degrees. Accurate orientation of the dial was not critical, however, and the Pole star was normally used for aligning the diptych at night for use as a moon dial (see below).

The motion of the earth and its effect on day length and the altitude of the sun can be understood more clearly with reference to figures 3 and 4. When the earth is in position 1 (around March 21), the sun lies directly over the equator at noon. Its declination is therefore zero. The length of night and day is twelve hours each along all the earth's latitudes. This is known as the *spring equinox*. After this date, the days become longer and the nights shorter in the northern hemisphere. At position 2 (June 21), the *summer solstice,* the sun has reached its greatest distance and maximum declination northwards from the equator, the Tropic of Cancer. At noon the sun's rays are directly overhead there. The North pole has twenty-four hours of daylight and the South pole twenty-four hours of darkness.

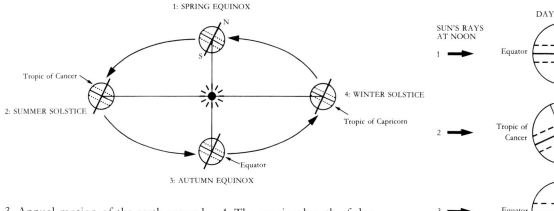

3 Annual motion of the earth around the sun
The earth rotates anti-clockwise about its own axis every 24 hours and moves anti-clockwise around the sun, taking a year to complete its circuit. At positions 1 and 3, the spring equinox *and* autumn equinox, *the sun lies directly over the equator at noon. At position 2, the* summer solstice, *the sun at noon is directly overhead at the Tropic of Cancer. At position 4, the* winter solstice, *it is directly overhead at the Tropic of Capricorn at noon.*

4 The varying length of day
1 and 3 show the spring and autumn equinoxes, when the lengths of night and day are 12 hours each along all the earth's latitudes. 2 is the summer solstice; at the North pole there are 24 hours of daylight, while at the South pole there are 24 hours of darkness. 4 is the winter solstice when there is continuous night at the North pole and continuous daylight at the South pole.

At position 3 (September 23), the *autumn equinox,* the sun is once more over the equator at noon, and days and nights are of equal length everywhere. It then moves progressively southwards until it reaches its greatest distance south of the equator. By position 4 (December 21), the sun's rays at noon are directly overhead at this latitude, the Tropic of Capricorn. At the South pole there are twenty-four hours of daylight while there are twenty-four hours of night at the North pole. The date marks the *winter solstice* of the northern hemisphere, the shortest day, and the summer solstice of the southern hemisphere. In figure 4 light and dark areas show how the lengths of day vary on the solstices and equinoxes

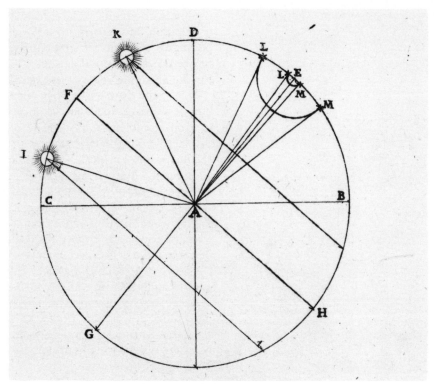

5 The changing declination of the sun
A marks the position of the earth, K the Tropic of Cancer, I the Tropic of Capricorn, E the celestial pole. Engraving from Johann Philipp von Wurzelbaur, Opera Geographico-Astronomica *(Nuremberg, 1728), Appendix.* GNM, Bibl. Nw 2149 f.

at different latitudes.   Figure 5 shows the angular distance of the sun from the equator at the Tropics of Cancer (K) and Capricorn (I).   E marks the celestial North pole, the large arc LM indicates the changing position of the pole of the ecliptic, and the small arc LM that of the Pole star as the earth's axis moves.   (For basic introductions to the principles of gnomonics and the relevant astronomy, see *History of Technology,* vol. 3, 558–619; Mayall & Mayall; Rohr; Schroeder; Waugh.)

Using the diptych: string-gnomon dials

In order to set the string-gnomon dials on a Nuremberg diptych dial correctly, three conditions have to be observed (figs 6 and 7).   First, the lower leaf must be placed exactly parallel to the horizon while the upper leaf forms a right angle vertically to it.   To facilitate the alignment, a small plumb-bob is sometimes incorporated into the upper leaf (fig. 8).

The second condition is that the gnomon must be aligned with the *meridian* of the place where it is being used.   This is an imaginary line which runs in a north-south direction through the location and the poles.   When the sun is over the meridian of any spot, it is noon, local time.   It is called 'local time' as no two points will share the same time unless they are on the same meridian.   Places on the same meridian have the same *longitude* as each other, the angular distance west or east from a standard meridian (fig. 9).   Since 1884, the standard meridian has been that which passes through Greenwich (0°).   Before this date, the standard meridian was either that given by Ptolemy, whose longitude zero ran through the Fortunate Islands (assumed by Renaissance scholars to be the Canaries), or else varied according to national or regional preference.   The cosmographer Johann Schöner (1477–1547), for example, took Nuremberg as his standard of 0° (Gallois, 111).   As the earth rotates, places at different longitudes have noon at different times, with 15° of longitude corresponding to one hour's difference.   (There are 360° in a circle and there are twenty-four hours in a day, hence in each hour the earth moves through 15°.)

SUN'S
RAYS

49°

6 Correct alignment of the diptych
The angle of the string is first adjusted to the latitude where the man is using the diptych (in this case, 49° N). The instrument is then held (or placed on a flat surface) so that the leaves are at right angles to each other and the lower leaf is level and, therefore, parallel to the horizon. By reference to the compass the string gnomon is aligned in a north-south direction. The rays of the sun now cast the shadow of the string gnomon onto the vertical and horizontal dial plates to give a correct reading of the hour.

SUN'S RAYS

7 Use of the diptych: the vertical and horizontal string-gnomon dials
The lower leaf is parallel to the earth's horizon and aligned in a north-south direction. The string gnomon is adjusted to form an angle with the lower leaf equivalent to the latitude where it is being used (shown here as 49° N), and is therefore parallel to the earth's axis.

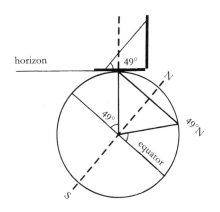

horizon   49°

N

49°N

equator

S

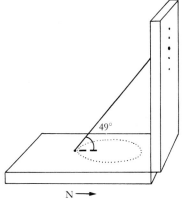

49°

N

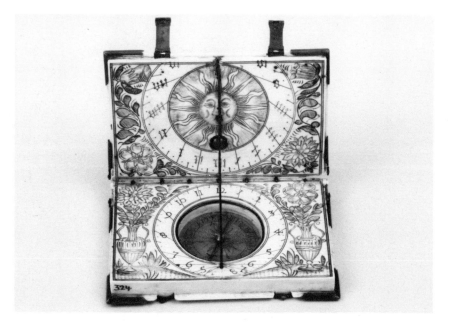

8 Maker unknown (possibly Conrad Karner), c. 1617
A silver plumb-bob is suspended from the upper leaf to facilitate the alignment of the lower leaf in the horizontal and the upper leaf in the vertical plane.
Cat. 32.

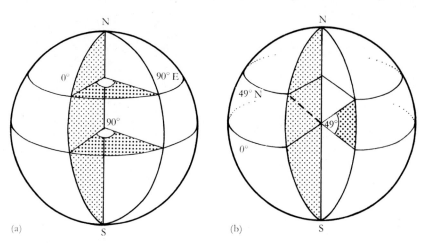

9 The earth's co-ordinates
(a) Longitude *refers to the angular distance west or east from a standard meridian, which today is taken as the part of the great circle line between the poles which passes through Greenwich Observatory (0°). The line of longitude shown here is about 90° E.*
(b) Latitude *refers to the angular distance north or south from the equator (0°). The latitude marked here is 49° N, approximately that of Nuremberg.*

A portable direction sundial without any means of finding north is thus obviously of limited use. The incorporation of a magnetic needle and compass marked with the cardinal points (north, south, east and west) ensures that the gnomon can be correctly aligned on any occasion. One problem, however, in relying on a compass needle for finding north, is the fact that magnetic north usually deviates from true north by several degrees (fig. 10). This phenomenon is known as *magnetic variation,* or declination.

During the sixteenth and early seventeenth centuries magnetic north in Europe lay to the east of true north by several degrees (varying in different places), drifting towards zero around 1650; it then gradually moved towards the west. The history of the discovery of magnetic variation and its documentation by scholars and explorers has been dealt with elsewhere and need not concern us here (Balmer; Körber, 66–76; H. Wagner; Waters, 24–6). It is clear, however, that the concept of variation was familiar to the Nuremberg compass-makers from a very early period. The compass bowls of their ivory sundials are almost always marked with a north-south line offset for magnetic variation. In instruments of the sixteenth and early seventeenth centuries the line is usually offset to the east by between

10 Magnetic variation
Effect of variation on the magnetic compass needle; shown at different positions on the earth, looking down from the North pole. From Levinius Hulsius, Descriptio et usus viatorii et horologii solaris *(Nuremberg, 1597), after sig. D5ᵛ.*
BL, 569 a. 15.

about 5–15°, while in the smallest diptychs of the late seventeenth century the line is offset to the west by a few degrees. In theory at least, when the needle points to this offset line, the noon hour line and string gnomon are directed towards the north. In practice, of course, since variation changes according to both time and place, the use of this method would have been at best an approximation.

The third condition to be observed is that the gnomon must be placed at an angle which is equal to the latitude of the place where the instrument is being used. *Latitude* refers to the angular distance north or south from the equator (0°) (fig. 9). Latitude can be determined astronomically by measuring the altitude of the sun as it passes over the meridian, consulting tables (ephemerides) for its declination, and finding the complement (the zenith distance) of this corrected value. It can also be found by measuring the altitude of the celestial pole. The term 'pole-degree' (*Polus Grad*) was frequently used for latitude in the period.

Because of the necessary alignment between gnomon and latitude, sundials with fixed gnomons can be used effectively only in one particular latitude, unless, of course, some form of table is available to make the right corrections. A portable dial intended for use by a traveller is obviously more practical if it can be used in a variety of locations without lengthy calculations. Since any movement north or south means a change of latitude, the sundial must be adaptable in some way to make it accurate for different latitudes.

The most common method used on the Nuremberg diptychs is to provide several holes on the vertical leaf through which the string gnomon can be attached. Each hole is marked with a particular degree of latitude, usually ranging from about 42° to 54° north, which embraces most of Europe (see fig. 39 below). The string can be moved to the hole which corresponds most closely to the latitude where the dial is being used. A series of hour lines for the different locations is also provided. Many diptychs incorporate a table of cities and towns with their latitudes for the traveller to consult. The source of these latitude tables and their accuracy are questions which are considered more fully in Chapter six.

When all these conditions are satisfied, and the sun is shining, the correct local apparent time can be determined with a fair degree of accuracy. (Time by the sun will often be different from mean time as it was later commonly taken from the mechanical clock; because the sun's apparent motion through the ecliptic is not uniform, the length of the solar day varies slightly throughout the year). On a horizontal dial the hour lines usually run from 5 a.m. to 12 noon to 7 p.m., and on a vertical dial from 6 a.m. to 12 noon to 6 p.m. The hours may be marked in Arabic or Roman numerals.

Using the diptych: equatorial and polar dials

So far, the diptychs have been described as consisting simply of vertical and horizontal string-gnomon dials hinged at right angles to each other. Some of these instruments are also designed to function as equatorial dials. In an *equatorial* or *equinoctial dial* a thin rod is set perpendicular in the centre of the dial plate which is aligned with the equator (fig. 11).

To use the equatorial dial on a diptych, a pin gnomon must be inserted through a special hole in the upper leaf. The diptych is aligned to the meridian by means of the compass, and the upper leaf is then tilted downwards from the vertical through an angle equal to the latitude of the place at which it is to be used. (The angle the dial plate is now tilted from the horizontal is equal to the co-latitude, i.e. 90° − latitude.) To set this

SUN'S RAYS

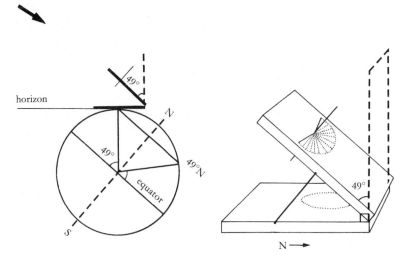

11 Use of the diptych: the equatorial dial
The lower leaf is parallel to the earth's horizon and aligned with the meridian. The upper leaf is tilted from the vertical through an angle equal to the latitude (here 49° N) so that the upper dial plate is aligned parallel with the equator. The gnomon, perpendicular to the dial plate, is parallel to the earth's axis. The sun's rays will only shine on the upper face of the dial between March 21 and September 23, the spring and autumn equinoxes.

angle correctly, which aligns the dial plate with the equator, a brass index arm attached to the upper plate is positioned against a scale on the lower leaf (fig. 12).   As a consequence of this equatorial alignment, the hour lines 4 to 12 to 8 are spaced uniformly 15° apart on the dial surface.

Since the dial plate is parallel to the equator, and the sun is north of the equator for only half the year, the sun will shine on the upper face of the properly-aligned dial only between March 21 and September 23.   In order to use it during winter the gnomon is extended through the dial plate, where another series of hour lines is marked, which are numbered anti-clockwise with noon still at the bottom reading 6 to 12 to 6, or 5 to 12 to 7.

Another type of dial, found only rarely on these diptychs, is the *polar dial*.   This is a direction dial which can be used in any latitude with the aid of the compass.   In this case, however, the diptych must be turned around so that the hinge points due south instead of north (fig. 13).   The outside of the upper leaf is marked with the polar dial face, where the hour lines lie parallel to one another (fig. 14).   The pin gnomon is inserted so that it is perpendicular to the dial plate, which has to be in the same plane as the earth's axis.   The upper leaf therefore must be tilted from the vertical by the co-latitude of the user's location.   Thus, from its closed

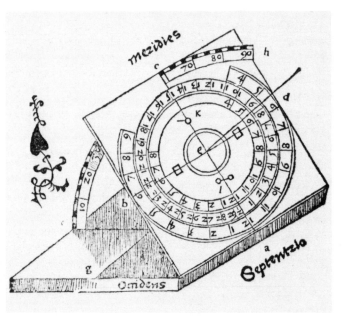

12 The equatorial dial
The angle of the equatorial dial plate is set by means of an index arm. Sebastian Munster, Rudimenta mathematica *(Basel, 1551), 229.*
RAS.

position, the upper leaf would have to be opened out from the horizontal through an angle equal to the latitude.

Although that portion of the European literature discussing polar dials which we have been able to consult refers only to the use of a bar gnomon parallel to the earth's axis, a pin gnomon (where the tip of the shadow indicates time) can also be used.   An example of such a pin-gnomon polar dial is that found on the astronomical compendium made in Damascus in A.H. 767 (1365/6) by ᶜAli b. Ibrāhīm b. ash-Shāṭir, which apparently also had a compass needle, now missing.   (See L. Janin and D. A. King, 'Ibn al-Shāṭir's Sandūq al-Yawāqīt: An Astronomical "Compendium"', *Journal for the History of Arabic Science*, 1 (1977), 187–256.)

The thin rod used as the gnomon for the equatorial dial or the polar dial is kept in a special compartment in the lower leaf of the diptych which has a brass cover to secure it.   Very few of the instruments still have this rod.

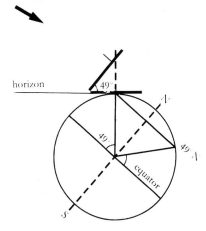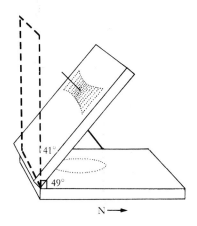

13 Use of the diptych: the polar dial
The lower leaf is parallel to the earth's horizon and aligned with the meridian, but now in a south-north orientation. The dial plate on the outside of the upper leaf must be parallel to the earth's axis, and so is tilted from the vertical by an angle equal to the co-latitude (90° minus 49° = 41°).

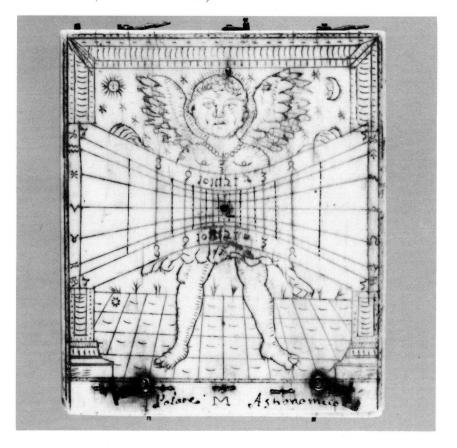

14 Georg Hartmann, 1562
Leaf 1a with polar dial, where the hour lines lie parallel to one another. The dial is also marked to indicate the sun's declination according to season.
Cat. 24. *(See also Plate II and fig. 72).*

Types of hours

The main dial plates of the Nuremberg sundials are usually marked into hourly divisions, equal hours a.m. and p.m. (*ante meridiem* and *post meridiem* = before and after the middle of the day). While this might now seem an obvious procedure, we must remember that this system of dividing the day into twenty-four equal hours has by no means always been observed. In the early modern period there were several systems of time reckoning employed in Europe (Vincent & Chandler). Until the fourteenth century the most widespread system used was to divide the daylight period into twelve equal parts and the night into twelve equal parts (6 o'clock = noon and midnight). The length of a daylight hour thus differed from the night hour (except at the equinoxes), and both varied according to season. These changing hours were known by several names: unequal, temporal, canonical, and planetary hours all refer to this type of system.

From the middle of the fourteenth century a new system of reckoning first appeared in Italian cities, and its use gradually became adopted in other parts of Europe. This was to divide the full day and night period into twenty-four equal hours. The reason for this change was the invention of the weight-driven clock, which could not easily be adjusted for measuring unequal hours. In turn this led to a development in sundial design. Sundials, which were relatively accurate devices, now had to be able to indicate equal hours so that they could be used to correct the less precise mechanical clocks (Turner, 23–6). (To adjust a clock accurately a sundial required the use of a table to convert apparent solar time to mean time.)

There were several ways of numbering the equal hours. It is notable that the Nuremberg diptych dials usually provide markings for at least three of these types, as well as for unequal hours.

Common, German or **French** hours, in Latin known as ***horae communes.*** Here the hours are divided into two groups of twelve, one beginning at midday, the other at midnight. Most domestic timekeeping today still follows this system. The vertical and horizontal string-gnomon dials on almost all of the diptychs are calibrated for these hours. The hours in a twelve-hour system were sometimes called 'small' hours (*Kleine Uhr*).

Italian, Bohemian, or **Welsch** (i.e. foreign) hours, also described in Latin as ***horae ab occasu solis*** (hours from the setting of the sun). As the Latin makes clear, Italian hours are reckoned from sunset, beginning with 0 and ending with 24 at the same point the following day. Daylight hours are numbered at the top end of the scale. The curved hour lines on the dial plate are usually numbered from about 10 to 24.

Babylonian, Greek hours, or ***horae ab ortu solis,*** start with sunrise as 0 and end at 24 the following sunrise. Daylight hours are thus represented by lower figures, with the dial calibrated from 0 or 1 to 16.

Nuremberg hours, or ***horae norimbergenses,*** combine both these systems together. Hour reckoning begins at either sunrise or sunset. Daylight hours by this method are equivalent to Babylonian hours, numbered from 1 upwards, while night hours are reckoned by the Italian system, which also begin at 1 after sunset. It is for this reason that a dial calibrated for Babylonian hours is sometimes marked with the inscription 'Nuremberg hours'. The hours in all these twenty-four hour systems were called 'large' or 'great' hours (*Grosse Uhr*). On most of the ivory diptychs, Italian and Babylonian hours are found on small pin-gnomon dials in the horizontal leaf. In many cases the two systems are inscribed in a single scaphe, one set of numerals and hour lines in red, the other coloured in black (Plate III).

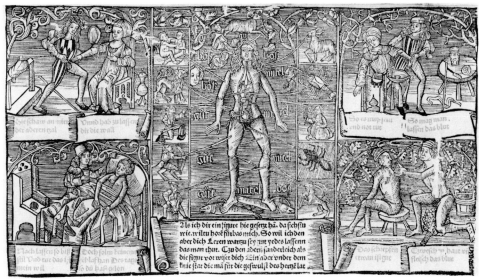

15 Zodiac man
Woodcut with central figure showing the influence of the signs of the zodiac and the planets over the parts of the body, with accompanying scenes of medical practice. 1496.
BSB, Einblatt-Kal. 1496.

Unequal or **planetary hours,** if included, are usually marked on the inside of the vertical leaf and calibrated 1 to 12. In addition a *planetary table* is sometimes included (Plate XII). Based on astrological principles, this table indicates which planet rules over each hour of each day of the week. The order of both the days of the week and the hours of the day was based on the seven known planets arranged in the supposed order of decreasing distance from the earth: Saturn, Jupiter, Mars, Sun, Venus, Mercury, Moon. Such information was important for medical practitioners, astrologers and others whose activities were guided by the stars (fig. 15).

Seasons and zodiac symbols

Many of the diptychs incorporate a vertical altitude dial with a horizontal pin-gnomon which indicates the length of day according to the season of the year (fig. 16). The pin is usually located at the top centre of the inside

16 Jacob Karner, 1639
The top part of the vertical leaf functions as an altitude dial with pin gnomon (now missing). The path traced by the tip of the gnomon across the dial varies according to the season, indicated by zodiac symbol. The numbers 8–16 and 16–8 refer to day and night length respectively. The dial is also calibrated for unequal or planetary hours 1–12 (6 = noon). On the lower leaf are two horizontal pin-gnomon dials. The one on the left is for Italian hours, calibrated from 10–23, while the other is for Babylonian hours, calibrated from 1–14.
Cat. 9.

upper leaf. As already explained, the declination of the sun varies throughout the year. Both the length of shadow and the path it traces across the dial plate changes according to the sun's declination as it moves along the ecliptic.

At the times of the equinoxes, when day and night length are equal, the tip of the shadow cast by the horizontal pin moves in a straight line running due west-east. This line is usually marked 12 to indicate the number of daylight hours. At all other times of the year the path is curved, according to season. The longest day, or summer solstice, is marked by the lowest line, which is convex towards the gnomon. Since the sun is at its highest, and bearing in mind the gnomon is horizontal, it naturally casts the longest shadow, and there are 16 daylight hours. At the winter solstice the shadow is very short, and traces a convex line around the gnomon which is marked for 8 daylight hours. The remaining lines are marked between these three. On some diptychs numbers are also given for night hours, which run from 16 to 8 in reverse order to daylight hours.

What of the other symbols? These represent the signs of the zodiac (from the Greek word *zōion* meaning 'animal'). This is an imaginary band, 8° wide, on each side of the ecliptic. The sun, moon and planets appear always to remain within this band as they move through their orbits. The band is thought of as being divided into twelve segments of 30° each, with each segment being named after the constellation of stars it once contained within it (fig. 17). Because of the precession of the

17 Armillary sphere showing the Ptolemaic system
The earth is fixed at the centre while the planets move along the ecliptic, which cuts the equator at an angle of approximately 23½ degrees. As the sun completes its annual orbit it passes through the various segments or houses of the zodiac, each named after a particular star constellation. Johannes Regiomontanus, Epitome *(Venice, 1496), sig. a 3ᵛ.* RAS.

equinoxes (due to the wobble in the earth's rotation), these signs no longer coincide with the constellations of fixed stars after which they were named.   The sun passes from one segment or house of the zodiac to the next around the twentieth day of each calendar month.

Reading from the top right of the dial plate (of a vertical pin-gnomon dial) in an anti-clockwise direction, the symbols represent the following signs: Capricorn (goat; the first day marks the winter solstice), Aquarius (water carrier), Pisces (fishes), Aries (ram, the first sign of the Zodiac, the first day marks the spring equinox), Taurus (bull), Gemini (twins), Cancer (crab; the first day marks the summer solstice), Leo (lion), Virgo (virgin), Libra (scales), Scorpio (scorpion), Sagittarius (archer).   In most cases these signs are represented pictorially, but sometimes the alchemical/astrological symbols are used instead.

Using the moon: the lunar volvelle

For all its flexibility, the diptych described thus far is limited to use during daylight hours.   In order to be really helpful to the traveller, it is also necessary for an instrument to be able to show the correct time at night.   The problem is that the motions of the sun and moon are different, and so their shadows are also affected.   The moon revolves around the earth approximately every $29\frac{1}{2}$ days, a *lunar month*, and as it does so its illuminated part apparently varies in size.   Successive lunar appearances are known as the 'phases' of the moon.   On the diptychs they are normally represented as: the new moon, the first quarter, the full moon, the last quarter.   The time taken for the moon to go around the ecliptic is approximately 27 days, a *sidereal month* (figs 18 and 19).

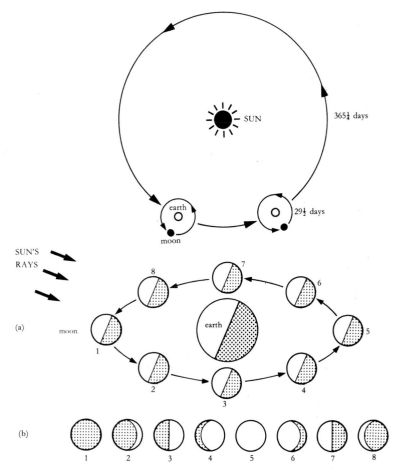

18 Difference between solar and lunar time
The moon revolves around the earth approximately every $29\frac{1}{2}$ days, a lunar month *or period from new moon to new moon. The earth revolves around the sun approximately every $365\frac{1}{4}$ days, a* sidereal *year.*

19 The phases of the moon
As the moon moves in orbit around the earth the illuminated portion seen from the earth varies in size. (a) shows that exactly half the moon is illuminated by the sun's rays all the time, regardless of its position. (b) shows what the moon looks like, seen from the earth, during its different positions. 1 is the new moon, 3 is the first quarter, 5 the full moon, 7 the last quarter.

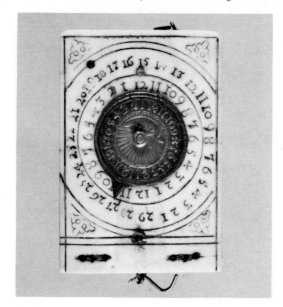

20 Possibly Karner workshop; late
17th/early 18th century
*Leaf 1a. The lunar volvelle comprises a
brass disc with pointer and solar hour
index (1–12, 1–12), an inner circle
marked for lunar hours (1–12, 1–12)
and an outer circle for indicating the days
after the new moon (1–29).*
Cat. 6.

On an outer leaf of many of these instruments, a device which can
convert lunar time to solar time is found, known as the *lunar volvelle*.   This
usually consists of a brass disc with pointer, marked with an hour index
1 to 12, 1 to 12, and two concentric rings on the ivory, the inner one
marked for hours 1 to 12, 1 to 12, and the outer one for days 1 to $29\frac{1}{2}$
(fig. 20).   For a week or so before and after the full moon, if it is not
obscured by cloud, the moonlight is bright enough to take an hour-
reading using the string-gnomon dial.   At night, the gnomon can be
aligned by using the Pole star, the tail of the constellation Ursa Minor (the
Little Bear), rather than by means of the compass (fig. 21).   The pointer
of the brass disc is first set to the number of days which have elapsed since
the new moon.   Since this information is not always available to the
traveller, the brass disc may be pierced so that when it is rotated it reveals
a representation of the moon at different phases which can be matched to
the real moon (see fig. 57).   The number on the brass disc which corresponds to the hour-reading from the sundial is then pointing to the correct
time of the night marked on the ivory hour ring.   This method, it must
be said, is relatively inaccurate.

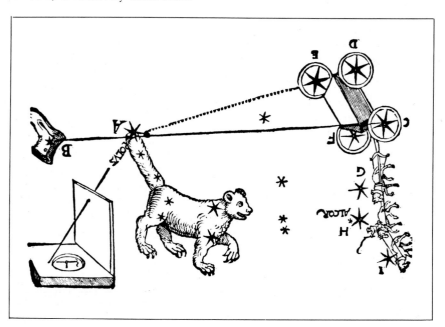

21 Alignment of the string-gnomon
(pole-string) with the Pole star
Peter Apian, Folium Populi
(Ingolstadt, 1533).
RAS.

Epact tables

On some of the dials, there are two more series of numbers in rings arranged outside those for the lunar volvelle. These are *epact tables,* and can be used, in conjunction with tables of an almanac, to calculate the date of Easter. Following the law of the Latin or Western churches, Easter Day falls on the first Sunday after the first full moon after the spring equinox. Because the moon and sun have different cycles – the lunar year being shorter than the solar year by about eleven days – the date of Easter changes from year to year. An epact number is the number of days past the new moon on the first day of January in any year of a nineteen-year cycle, the period before the sun and moon are again in the same relative positions in the zodiac. The epact number can also be used to predict the nights when there will be a moon, and to determine the ebbing and flowing of the tides which are affected by the moon's motion (Vincent & Chandler, 381–4).

Why are there two sets of numbers? This requires further historical explanation. Until 1582, the calendrical system used throughout Europe was the Julian calendar. Introduced by Julius Caesar in 46 B.C., it had three years of 365 days and a fourth of 366 days, the leap year. Since this calculation was not quite accurate, by the sixteenth century there was an urgent need for calendrical reform. In 1582 Pope Gregory XIII imposed a new system which took account of the irregular motions of the sun and earth more exactly. The Gregorian calendar skips one leap year in every centurial year that is not divisible by 400.

The Gregorian calendar was adopted in most Catholic countries of Europe between 1582 and 1587. Protestant countries, however, were reluctant to adopt the new system immediately. The English authorized its adoption as late as 1752. The situation in Germany, divided into Protestant and Catholic states, was particularly complicated. The Protestant states used the Julian calendar until 1700 (*History of Technology,* vol. 3, 578–91). It is not surprising to find that epact numbers given on the portable compass dials are given for both the Gregorian and Julian calendars.

Wind rose

For the sake of completeness, the accessories found on the outside of the upper leaf of many diptychs should also be mentioned; namely the *wind rose, compass viewing-hole, index arm* and (usually missing) the *wind vane.* The wind or compass rose is usually divided into four cardinal points, subdivided to sixteen or thirty-two divisions known as rhumbs of the wind (Taylor I; fig. 22). The compass viewing-hole allows the compass needle to be seen when the diptych is closed.

It is interesting to note that the wind rose was occasionally described as a 'mariner's compass' by the compass-makers themselves. Some diptychs (e.g. Cat. 50), are inscribed with the following words: 'HIC MARINVS COMPASSVS SEMITAM TERRA MARIQVE OSTEN-DIT' (This maritime compass shows the path on land as well as at sea). The use of the term 'mariner's compass' to describe the wind rose has led some (e.g. Werner, 107–8) to assume that the Nuremberg compass-makers actually produced navigational aids. It is more likely that the only type of 'compass' manufactured in Nuremberg was the portable dial for overland direction-finding or surveying.

The names of the eight Mediterranean winds, usually in the form 'Tramontan | Greco | Levante | Sirocho | Ostro | Lebechio | Ponente | Mastro' are found on the upper leaf, or else sometimes in the compass bowl. The direction of the wind in the land mass of Europe is critical

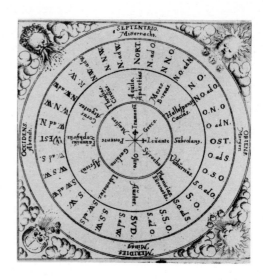

22 (left) wind rose, index arm and compass viewing hole on a diptych; (right) compass directions.
Levinius Hulsius, Descriptio et usus viatorii et horologii solaris *(Nuremberg, 1597), before sig. C, facing sig. A2.*
BL, 569 a. 15.

to the weather; each wind has its own particular characteristics. The Sirocco, for example, is a warm, southerly wind which brings air from the hot desert interior of northern Africa. The Maestro or Mistral is a cold northerly wind, while the Levante is an easterly wind. The importance of wind direction for temperature and the weather is explicitly indicated on some of the dials which are marked with the following information: 'SCHON DRVCK | HEITER KALT | WARM HEITTER | SCHON MIT MESIG | WARM FEICHT | RENGISCH [*sic*] | KALT FEICHT | SCHNEIG' (Fair dry, bright cold, warm bright, fair average, warm humid, rainy, cold humid, snowy; fig. 109). The Latin terms for the four cardinal points (*Septentrio, Occasus, Meridies, Ortus*) may also be included on the compass or elsewhere on the surface or edge of the leaf.

The wind vane, kept in a compartment in the lower leaf when not in use, is inserted into a hole at the centre of the compass rose. The wind is meant to blow the vane around, thereby indicating its direction, to which the index arm can be set accordingly.

What were the diptychs for?

The multiple functions of the diptychs described here make it obvious that these instruments were much more than time-telling devices. But were the accessories really all used and understood by their owners? Such issues are complex and deserve further investigation. Some attempt to answer them is made in later chapters, which seek to place the diptychs in their social, economic, technical and aesthetic contexts.

For the moment it can be said that the diptychs could certainly have been used for determining local time reasonably accurately and for basic orientation with a map. But they represented far more than this. Nuremberg dials were designed to be universal and represented the 'state of the art' in the popular technology of the period, in much the same way that a multi-functional watch or pocket calculator combined with radio and alarm might today. They measured time by at least two hour systems and provided the means of converting between them. The fact that they could in principle be adjusted according to latitude and were marked with magnetic variation also reveals a commitment to accuracy wherever the instrument might be used. In other words, they were the product of an age of expanding horizons and new understanding.

CHAPTER TWO

Why were they made of ivory and where did it come from?

It might seem surprising that time-telling instruments should be made of ivory. Ivory, after all, is a material associated with the arts and crafts rather than science or precision technology. Why did the people manufacturing the diptychs choose ivory as a material for their product? Was it the only material that they used? Did other craftsmen in Nuremberg also use ivory during the same period?

Ivory as a material

The suitability of ivory as a material for the manufacture of portable sundials can be considered first. The term 'ivory' generally refers to dentine, the inner mineralized tissue of teeth which is particularly abundant in the tusks of certain mammals. Elephant tusks, which are modified, continuously-growing incisor teeth of the upper jaw, are the most common source of ivory, but others which have been exploited over the centuries include the tusks of mammoth, walrus, hippopotamus and narwhal (a type of Arctic whale). The Nuremberg sundials are usually made from elephant ivory, and very occasionally from bone. (For general introductions to ivory, see Burack; MacGregor; Maskell; G. Williamson.)

Elephant ivory has a distinctive close-grained texture conditioned by the way that the growing tusk is formed. The following paragraphs on the growth of ivory are based on Brown & Kelly, whose research indicates that earlier accounts may now have to be modified. In the long axis of the tusk, alternating coloured shaded bands of white and cream may be seen, which in a cross-section give a characteristic 'engine-turned' appearance (fig. 23). These bands or apparent layers occur because the ivory, which consists of heavily mineralized fibres, is deposited around the elongated extensions (processes) of the closely packed ivory-forming cells, each of which lies within its own minute tube. The processes are continuously being lengthened. These cells commence laying down the ivory at the periphery of the tusk, and as they do so, slowly migrate towards the central or pulpal zone. In the oldest part of the tusk, towards the tip, this central zone is completely filled with ivory. A comparatively thin layer of 'bark' or cementum is deposited on the external surface of the ivory, and serves, with its attached fibres, to secure the tusk in its socket (fig. 24).

According to most textbooks, there are two main types of elephant ivory. The first is from West Africa and is hard and close-grained. The second, mainly from East Africa and India, is considered to be whiter and softer. While the distinction may be apparent in fresh tusks, in practice it is difficult to establish with any certainty which type of ivory has been used for an object made hundreds of years ago. This is the case with the diptych dials.

A tusk has to be seasoned and dried properly before use, to allow for

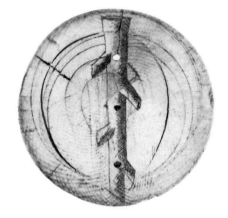

23 Ivory compass dial, probably Nuremberg, 16th/17th century. *Unusually, this dial is made from a cross-section of a tusk; the milling marks are clearly visible on the lower surface.* Cat. 60.

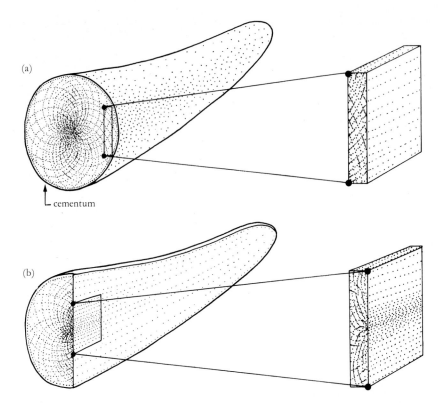

24 Characteristics of elephant ivory
A cross-section of the tusk shows the milling marks which appear as overlapping arcs of different diameters. The diptychs are usually made from blocks cut from the tusk's long axis; (a) the edges of the shorter sides of the tablets show the milling marks, (b) the flat surfaces show alternating cream and white bands.

natural shrinkage, otherwise it may later crack or warp.   It is also liable to crack if it is subjected to extremes of heat or cold.   Within these limits, however, it is a durable, resilient material.   Ivory can be cut and handled using the same hand tools as those used for wood, such as knives, gouges, files and saws (Ritchie, 13–25).   Since ivory is harder than most woods, however, these tools have to be relatively stronger.

Although there may be several superficial resemblances between wood and ivory, they are fundamentally different in their structure and their constituents.   Wood grows from inside out, while ivory grows from outside in.   Ivory is particularly suitable for detailed and intricate carving because of its continuous intermesh of closely packed, mineralized organic fibres.   In life these are organized around rows of parallel cell extensions, which when the ivory is dried, leave it filled with a mass of parallel, almost invisible tubes.   It is the arrangement of the fibres and their impregnation with minute interlocking crystals which, under normal circumstances, gives ivory its toughness and prevents it from fracturing.   Most important of all, this arrangement enables ivory to be cut in straight and curved planes in all directions.   Dyes and pigments can easily be applied to its porous surface, thereby allowing scope for colour and decoration.   It can readily be buffed to a smooth, shiny and permanent polish because of its fine structure.   With respect to sundials, the white to creamy colour makes an excellent background for detecting the fine shadows cast by the gnomons.   (For further remarks on the working of ivory, see Chapter five.)

Bone and its identification

Very few diptych dials appear to have been made from bone rather than ivory.   There are several explanations for this.   Bone, compared with ivory, is difficult to carve; it does not have the homogeneity of ivory and is more variable in its natural markings, often producing a texture suggesting that that surface is covered with fine cracks (fig. 25). Bone derived from bones of a size large enough to make a complete diptych dial has muscles and ligaments attached to it which have to be removed by cutting and boiling before use, a very time-consuming process. Most diptychs made from bone are of the smallest type, in which each leaf is composed of a thin 'sandwich' of bone with a centre of wood (e.g. fig. 49).

The roles of individual bones in the body determine their specific characteristics, which have consequences for the craftsman. As they form a continuous source of calcium salts necessary for the body's life system, bones incorporate two special types of cell on their internal and external surfaces; osteoclasts which break down the bone to release the calcium, and osteoblasts which replace it. Other cells within the substance of the bone (osteocytes) are responsible for maintaining its health and monitoring the needs of the body. In any given area of bone there are thousands of these cells, all of which are linked together by many fine extensions, around which the forming bone is laid down. All bone cells must communicate with the blood supply to receive nutriments and stimuli. A few large blood vessels and many thousand minute ones traverse the hard compact bone, the outer part of a bone from which a diptych leaf could be cut.

Once ivory has been formed, its structure remains essentially unaltered, with the rhythmic lines and bands of deposition clearly defined in a distinct and readily-seen grainy pattern. Bone, on the other hand, is constantly modified to take account of the stresses to which it is exposed and other biological demands, and alters as the animal becomes older. Occasionally the surface markings caused by the presence of blood vessels in bone can be put to good use and incorporated into the craftsman's design, but usually they are seen as disfiguring marks. When a thin section of bone is held up to the light, these marks can be seen. However, it is difficult in some instances to detect the differences between bone and ivory with the naked eye, and only with the aid of a magnifying glass can their respective biological markings be made out.

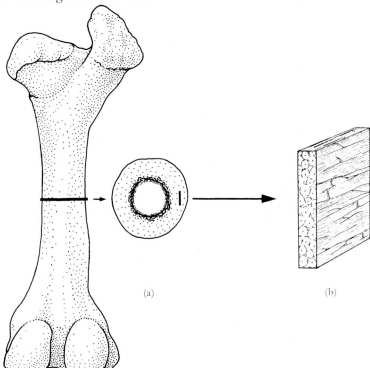

25 Characteristics of bone
An ox femur in cross section (a) shows the outer compact bone from which a thin leaf for a diptych could be cut. (b) an enlargement: the bone is composed of circular systems, in the centre of which run fine blood vessels. The fine cracks and irregular lines on the surface of a leaf of bone are caused by the presence of these vessels.

(a)   (b)

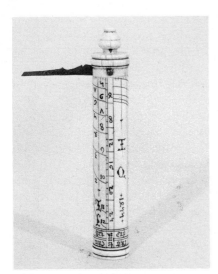

26 Ivory pillar dial, Nuremberg
*The inscription on the right bottom corner
appears to read '1455' rather than
'1477'.*
BNM, Inv. no. Phys 64.

Nuremberg ivory ware

For centuries ivory had been a luxurious commodity which, along with gold and other precious materials, was limited in availability to the devotional and secular needs of church, crown and nobility. It is notable that the diptych, which simply means two leaves hinged together, was already a characteristic form of ivory carving in Roman times. In the later Christian era altar pieces in the form of large diptychs, and even book covers, were produced in ivory (P. Williamson). From the late fifteenth century ivory gradually became used for a much wider range of secular and domestic objects. These were produced in relatively large numbers in several European centres, including Nuremberg (Burack, 22–3; Philippovich I).

Sundials

Sundials seem to have been among the first 'speciality' ivory products made commercially in Nuremberg. The earliest surviving Nuremberg ivory sundial is probably the small pillar dial now in the Bayerische Nationalmuseum, Munich (fig. 26; Zinner I, 123. Zinner's dating is 1455, while the museum's is 1477). It is stamped with an 'N', for Nuremberg. No other examples of Nuremberg ivory pillar dials are known to the present author.

When the first ivory sundials in diptych form were made is not known. The idea of making a folding instrument which resembled a writing tablet, book, or small box obviously gained popularity at a very early date. Most surviving diptychs, as is apparent from this exhibition, date from the mid-sixteenth century. Yet scattered among various museums in Europe and America there are a few diptych dials, mostly incomplete, which appear to have been made at the very end of the fifteenth century. This provisional dating is not inconsistent with the first reference to 'compass-makers' in Nuremberg city records of the 1480s and 1490s (see Table 6).

27 Ivory diptych dial, Nuremberg,
late 15th century
*Leaf 1a with relief carving of St. John
the Baptist; vertical and horizontal string-
gnomon dials calibrated for about 48°
latitude. The herring-bone grain of the
ivory is particularly unusual.*
BM, Reg. no. 77 5–21 23. *Courtesy of
the Trustees of the British Museum
(compare figs 28, 131).*

The British Museum has a complete example of one of these instruments (fig. 27).   It has a vertical and horizontal dial with hour lines calibrated for about 48° latitude for use with string gnomon and compass.   On the outside of the upper leaf is a relief carving of St. John the Baptist.   The herring-bone grain in this specimen of ivory is unusual; it is cut from a tusk which in the living animal had been exposed to some form of stress or temperature change.   Cat. 59 is the lower leaf of a similar dial which was found in the Thames (fig. 131).   Two upper leaves of dials of this type are also known: one is now in the Metropolitan Museum of Art, New York,

28 Upper leaf of ivory diptych dial, Nuremberg, late 15th century
Leaf 1a with relief carving depicting children at play.
New York, The Metropolitan Museum of Art, Rogers Fund, 1987 (1987.340). *All rights reserved, The Metropolitan Museum of Art.*

while the other is in the museum at Niort, France.   The carvings on these upper leaves, which depict children at play, are reminiscent of a style of woodcut found in Germany about 1480 (fig. 28; information provided in a personal communication by B. D. Boehm, Assistant Curator, Department of Medieval Art, Metropolitan Museum of Art, New York).

Although it is known from documentary evidence (Table 7) that the compass-makers used boxwood and pearwood as well as ivory for their instruments, only a very few wooden diptychs have been preserved.   The Germanische Nationalmuseum in Nuremberg has four (Zinner I, 310, 438, 484), but there are no similar examples in any of the major British collections.   However, a number of wooden horizontal dials with compasses, which are thought to have been made in Nuremberg in the sixteenth or seventeenth centuries, have already been found in archeological sites in England.   Two and part of a third one are now in the collection of the Museum of London.   One was found in Worship Street (London, EC2; fig. 132), the other complete one was among the items excavated by Martin Biddle at the site of Nonsuch Palace near Epsom, Surrey.   (Details of the latter by courtesy of Martin Biddle; information about the entire dig is forthcoming in *The Nonsuch Final Report,* Society of Antiquaries, HBMC.)   Ten wooden compass dials, of various shapes and designs, have been recovered from the wreck of the *Mary Rose* (information provided by Dr Margaret Rule, Research Director of the Mary Rose Trust, Portsmouth).   These findings suggest that such instruments, presumably of Nuremberg provenance, were used in England during the period.   Although it is undoubtedly true that most of the Nuremberg dials which survive today are ivory diptychs, this information would also indicate that there was a considerable supply of wooden sundials from Nuremberg.

29 Elaborately turned ivory goblets,
German, 17th century
BNM.

Other decorative objects

By the seventeenth century Nuremberg had become well-known for two
other types of ivory product.   The first of these was the large, elaborately
turned decorative piece, which resembled the type of work made by
silversmiths and goldsmiths (fig. 29).   Such objects were made with the
aid of machine lathes which were first developed in the sixteenth century.   These pieces – such as goblets and covers – demonstrated how
ivory could be turned, carved and engraved to rival the most delicate
silverware.   Most of them were made by a single Nuremberg family.   Members of the Zick dynasty who produced ivory carvings included
Jacob (d. 1589), Peter (1571–1629), Lorenz (1594–1666) and Stephan
(1639–1715) (Doppelmayr, 297, 299–300, 310; Philippovich I, 339,
349–57; Philippovich II, 301–14).   Turning in ivory was also a fashionable pursuit for royalty and members of the aristocracy during the
seventeenth and eighteenth centuries (Maurice; Gouk).

    Another group of ivory objects produced in Nuremberg and elsewhere
can be described as medical curiosities, specimens of which appear to have
been made in the workshop of Stephan Zick.   The most popular of these
was the anatomical manikin.   These small models, male and female, could
be taken apart to reveal the internal organs, and in the case of the female,
a foetus (fig. 30).   Another type of ivory model which could be taken
apart and reassembled for didactic purposes was the artificial eye (fig. 31;
Russell; Philippovich II, 248–53).

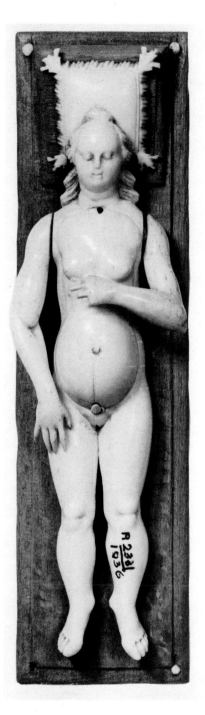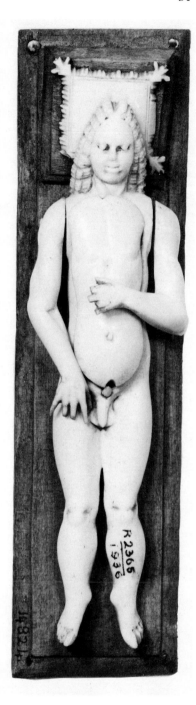

30 Pair of ivory anatomical manikins, 17th century
Probably made in the workshop of Stephan Zick (1639–1715).
London, Wellcome Institute Library, Inv. nos R2331/1936, R2365/1936.

31 Model of human eye in ivory by Stephan Zick
Johann Gabriel Doppelmayr, Historische Nachricht Von den Nürnbergischen Mathematicis und Künstlern *(Nuremberg, 1730), Table V.*
Photograph by Ian Jones, London.

Dieppe: a comparison

The diversity of ivory goods produced in Nuremberg is comparable to that found in Dieppe, another major centre for the manufacture of ivory products in the seventeenth and eighteenth centuries. As in the case of Nuremberg, particular families specialized in different types of object. For example, sundials were produced by Charles and Gabriel Bloud, Ephraim and Jacques Sénécal and François Saillot from the mid-seventeenth century (fig. 32). Other ivory goods included jewellery, vases, fans, chess sets, portrait medallions and statuettes. Dieppe was also a centre for watch-making. Following the Revocation of the Edict of Nantes in 1685, when Protestant worship was forbidden in France, Dieppe craftsmen fled with other Huguenots to England and introduced their trades in London. By the early eighteenth century London was developing as an important centre for both instrument making and ivory carving (Bazin; Milet; Murdoch).

32 Magnetic azimuth dial, Bloud type, second half of 17th century. *Ivory with brass fittings, silvered and silver volvelles; signed 'Fait et Invente par Charles Bloud ADieppe'.* W 787.

The ivory trade

So far it has simply been assumed that ivory was available to anyone who wished to use it. Where did it actually come from? The Nuremberg craftsmen would probably have bought their supplies from merchants and traders in the city itself. Nuremberg was a centre for the import of raw materials from all over the known world. Until the middle of the fifteenth century, elephant ivory was relatively scarce throughout northern Europe. From the end of the century, the supply gradually increased. During the next two hundred years, as the examples of Nuremberg and Dieppe reveal, ivory became an extremely fashionable material for all kinds of objects.

There was a good reason for the increased availability of ivory. The routes by which ivory was imported into Europe changed. For centuries, the chief route to Europe for African ivory, like that of gold and spices, had been overland across the Sahara desert to the North African coastal ports, and thence across the Mediterranean. The Arabs acted as middlemen between the Sudanese tradesmen, who collected ivory, gold and slaves from the unknown interior of Africa, and the Italian merchants of Venice and Genoa who held the European monopoly of all

Mediterranean trade. The Arabs were also in control of the ivory trade of Zanzibar and Mozambique. This was carried by ship from Ormuz to the Persian gulf and then moved by camel to Antioch, Constantinople and the Mediterranean ports where the Italian merchants operated (Barns; Bovill).

The problem with this trading system between East and West was that supplies of luxury items such as ivory, spices and gold were always uncertain and vulnerable to attack. Furthermore, any weakness of the Italian merchant trade was liable to be exploited by its European rivals. During the fifteenth century the dominance of the Venetians and Genoese in the Mediterranean was successfully challenged by Portugal and Spain. Italian trade and commerce suffered a series of set-backs in this period, due to wars and political upheaval. Turkish military and naval expansion in the East culminated in the fall of Constantinople in 1453, which temporarily severed overland communications with the West. The Venetians also lost their valuable trading privileges in the North African ports and were forced to raise the prices of their wares. Meanwhile, the political situation in Italy deteriorated, and a series of wars began in the north. The disruption of Italian commerce encouraged Portugal and Spain in particular to embark on a programme of exploration and commercial expansion.

Iberia's success and northern Europe's profit

The Iberian kingdoms were well placed to enter into competition with their Italian rivals and to seek alternative routes to Africa, India and the Far East. They had large fleets of smaller, cheaper ships designed for Atlantic fishing, new navigational expertise, and the backing of their kings. The capture of the Moroccan port of Ceuta by Prince Henry the Navigator in 1415 effectively marked the beginning of the exploration and exploitation of West Africa by the Portugese. It was probably at Ceuta that seamen first heard of the fabulously wealthy gold mines of West Africa. The powerful lure of such riches acted as strong incentive for subsequent voyages down the cost of Africa. (For further details see Parry; Bovill; Marque.)

The early phase of Portugese exploration of Africa was remarkably successful. In 1434 Cape Bojador was rounded, and the great rivers of Senegal and Gambia were discovered in 1444–6. The villages at the mouths of these rivers were to become major trading centres for gold dust, slaves, and ivory in the following centuries. Between 1469 and 1475 Fernando Gomes leased from the crown the rights to explore and trade along the coast of Guinea and reached as far as Benin. From his accession in 1481, King John II actively encouraged the development of the West African trade. An agreement had been reached with Spain in 1479 which allowed Portugal the monopoly of this trade. The fort of São Jorge da Mira was built in 1482, the first Portugese 'factory' for trade and defence in Africa. The immense profits which were to be made here proved an incentive for further expansion (fig. 33; Africa Atlas, 33).

Although the Portugese supplied the ships and some backing for this African trade, in practice most of the naval expertise and financial investment was provided by the Italians and south German bankers. When cargoes landed at Lisbon, they were bought in their entirety by these middlemen, who consequently made most of the profits. In the early years of direct trade, the crown kept the right to buy all the ivory imported from Guinea. After 1475, however, this condition was dropped and ivory could be bought by any merchant.

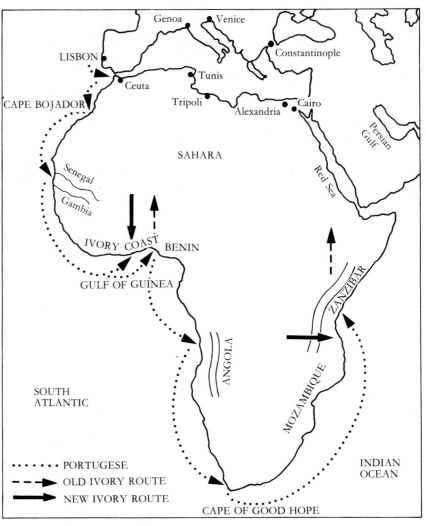

33 The ivory trade
Until the 15th century, ivory from East and West Africa went overland across the Sahara to the main North African ports and Constantinople. It was then shipped across the Mediterranean to Venice and Genoa, among the larger ports. As the Portuguese explored the African coast line, they established a series of trading forts. Ivory was among the goods now shipped to Europe via the Atlantic ports, notably Lisbon.

Meanwhile, Portugese sailors continued their exploration of the African coast. Angola was reached in 1484, and the Cape of Good Hope was rounded in 1487. During his first voyage to India in 1497–8, Vasco da Gama landed at Mozambique on the east coast of Africa. Portugese trade with East Africa was later properly established in the sixteenth century. Vasco da Gama's initial success at reaching the Malabar coast was followed by the conquest of Goa and Alberquerque in 1510, while Ceylon was reached in 1518.

By the early sixteenth century, then, Portugese traders had successfully established a flourishing trade in ivory on both the west and east coasts of Africa. There was a price to pay for this success. At this stage, Portugal had over-extended its resources and was unable to prevent Dutch, and subsequently English, merchants from breaking into this lucrative commerce in the seventeenth century. In the 1630s the Dutch took over most of the Portugese trading posts in Africa.

These events were to have a profound impact upon trade and commerce in both Africa and Europe. The traditional overland trade routes across Africa and their control by the Arabs were completely disrupted. African traders diverted their caravans of slaves, gold and ivory, which had previously crossed the Sahara, in order to deal directly with the Europeans on the western and eastern coasts. Their goods were imported to the Atlantic ports of Lisbon, Antwerp, and later Amsterdam and London. Ivory now flooded into Europe in much larger quantities than had ever been previously available.

In earlier centuries, what little ivory there had been must have come to Nuremberg overland from Venice via packboat and river. Now it came from Lisbon and Antwerp with the Nuremberg merchants themselves. We know from the trading account of 1558 of the Nuremberg merchant Lorenz Meder that in Lisbon, one hundredweight of elephant tusks cost 13 ducats or 1170 pfennigs, while in Antwerp, the same amount would have cost 1320 pfennigs. The pfennig, a silver coin, was the basic monetary unit in Nuremberg, while the ducat was one of the gold coins of international commerce. According to Meder's reckoning, the rate was 90 pfennigs per ducat (Kellenbenz I, 30–1, 158–60). The ivory would either have been transported from Lisbon by land and water across Spain and France, or upwards via the Rhine and the Main from Antwerp.

It is appropriate that the raw material used for the diptych dials became available as a result of the exploration and expansion out of which the demand for more accurate time-keeping and measuring instruments also arose. Why Nuremberg should have profited from these changes so rapidly is a question to be considered in the following chapter.

CHAPTER THREE

Why were they made in Nuremberg?

Nuremberg was one of the most important centres in Europe for the manufacture of luxury items. It specialized in metal goods, such as weapons and armour, locks, bells, clocks, musical and scientific instruments. Already by 1500 about one hundred and fifty different crafts were practised in the city (Strauss, 134–47; Stockbauer; Jegel). A group of compass-makers initially attempted to organize their craft in 1510, but the first documented legislation for the compass-makers, as for many other crafts, was only formalized by the city council in 1535 (H. Wagner, 181–2).

How did Nuremberg become such an important manufacturing centre in the first place? Why were scientific instruments, including sundials, developed in the city? The answers to these questions can perhaps be found by examining its economic and commercial development in the centuries before the sundials were first produced.

Growth of Nuremberg before 1500

Until the thirteenth century, Nuremberg had been a relatively unimportant town. German wealth and commerce was concentrated in the northern Hanseatic towns, including Hamburg and Lübeck. The balance was to change, however. By the early fifteenth century the Hanse had suffered a series of reverses from which they never recovered. Their trading empire, encompassing Scandinavia, England, the Low Countries and Russia, was fragmented as these countries gradually imposed restraints on foreign commerce and established their own independent trades. Trade was decentralized in the Netherlands. A further set-back to the League was the loss of the herring industry. The Baltic shoals migrated to the Atlantic where the Dutch fleets now dominated. Antwerp replaced Bruges as the major Atlantic port. Meanwhile, traders who had been blocked from the Baltic and certain land routes in northern Germany had created new trade routes which were to bring wealth to cities in the south of Germany. Nuremberg was now becoming a city of increasing commercial importance (*CEH*, 167–81; for further background to the European economic context, see Braudel; Cipolla; Kellenbenz II).

In the second half of the thirteenth century Nuremberg became a free imperial city and joined the League of Rhineland cities. From 1356 onwards, Nuremberg was a regular venue for Imperial Diets. In 1424 the imperial crown jewels were transferred to the city, and the imperial seal was deposited there while the emperor was absent from Germany. By 1431 Nuremberg had gained complete independence, and was allowed its own mint. These privileges made the city a major political centre, which in turn ensured its economic development. The regular influx of rich noblemen and other imperial representatives provided a guaranteed market for manufactured goods. The protection of the emperor meant that instead of becoming dominated by a local prince, the fate

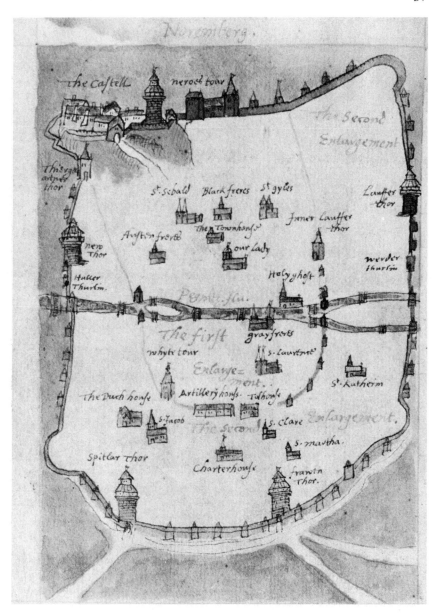

34 Map of the city of Nuremberg, by
William Smith, 1594
*Successive enlargments of the city
boundaries are clearly shown in this sketch.
They are tangible evidence of the growing
importance of Nuremberg.*
Nuremberg, Stadtbibliothek, Nor. H.
1142. Photograph by Foto Hilbinger
GmbH, Schwaig-Behringersdorf.

of many other towns, Nuremberg was able to extend its possessions and
interests.   This was also possible due to the relative peace which the
empire enjoyed during the period.   By 1500 the city held extensive territories outside its walls; its control over lands and inhabitants extended
over a radius of twenty-five miles (fig. 35; unless otherwise mentioned,
historical information about Nuremberg is taken from the following principal sources: Baron; Baxandall; Pfeiffer; Smith; Strauss).

The increasing independence and prosperity of Nuremberg was greatly
aided by the activities of its wealthy merchant patricians.   Together and
in competition with the Fuggers of Augsburg, the Nuremberg merchant
families established a network of credit and trading facilities that extended
throughout Europe and even to the New World.   A small number of
these families (notably the Tucher, Imhof, and Fürer) also secured an
interest in gold, silver, copper and tin mining which had a major impact
on the fortunes of the city (Braudel, 321–5).   As their wealth was based
predominantly on mercantile and banking facilities, they also generated a
demand for luxury goods, both for their own use and for export, which
were produced by the artisans and craftsmen who lived and prospered in
Nuremberg.

Another important element in Nuremberg's development during this period was the enormous increase in its population, particularly among skilled craftsmen. Following the Black Death in the fourteenth century – which had left Nuremberg almost completely unscathed – there had been a vast influx of people from the land, resulting in a pressure on existing handicrafts which led to craft specialization and heightened productivity. This process of urbanization and craft development was a feature of other south German cities such as Ulm, Augsburg and Regensburg. However, Nuremberg was the most populous and most successful of these in the sixteenth century. All these circumstances ensured the city's predominance in south German commercial and political affairs until the 1530s.

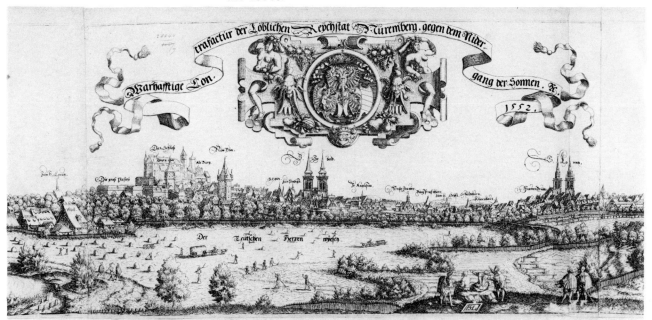

36 Nuremberg, view from the west by Hans Sebald Lautensack, 1552 BL, Maps 28840 (7).

35 Map showing a twenty-five mile radius around Nuremberg *Anonymous woodcut, c. 1545.* BL, Maps c 7 b. 18.

Social structure of Nuremberg

Nuremberg was remarkable not only for its territorial power but also for its unusual social structure. 1348 marked a turning-point in Nuremberg's history which led to a unique form of urban government. In that year, perhaps in response to the social turmoil instigated by the experience of the Black Death elsewhere in Europe, a revolt by the artisans and craftsmen of the city against the increasing power of the patricians was decisively overthrown. All guilds were abolished in 1349. From this point on only members of the patrician families exercised any significant power in the *Rat* or city council, making them the greatest urban aristocracy in Germany (fig. 37). Councillors from these families controlled courts and legal procedures, set taxes, and made rules concerning public order and all aspects of civic life.

During a period until about 1500, this form of 'benevolent despotism' worked in favour of the city and its trade and industry. Gradually, however, as we shall see in the case of the compass-makers, such control led to rigidity and fear of innovation. This rigidity was reflected in the decline of social mobility in the early sixteenth century, when entrance to the patrician class was effectively closed. It seems as though Lutheranism, adopted by the city in 1525, only reinforced this trend.

In 1500 the population of Nuremberg itself consisted of about twenty thousand people, with another twenty thousand living in close proximity

37 Seating plan of the Nuremberg
Rat or city council, 1677
Each shield identifies a member of a
patrician family or craft representative.
Anonymous engraving.
GNM, HB 2522.

(for a full account of Nuremberg's social structure, see Endres).   The
upper class consisted of forty-two ancient families, the *Geschlechter,* who
provided thirty-four out of forty-two members of the city council.   The
remaining eight members were selected from representatives of the most
important crafts, notably the building trades (Fleischmann).   In their
commercial activities, the patrician families were cautious and dealt with
safe commodities, rather than engaging in the more speculative enterprises
characteristic of the Fuggers.   This caution can be attributed to their dual
role as both merchants and city fathers concerned with the welfare of the
city.

Below the patricians, there were around four hundred *ehrbare Familien*
or 'Honourable Families'.   These occupied city offices and lower council

posts, but were effectively excluded from real political power. Members of this group were merchants, civil servants, doctors and law-yers. Together with the patricians they made up six to eight per cent of the population.

There was a substantial 'middle class' of master craftsmen and lesser tradesmen in the city. In the mid-sixteenth century there were over five thousand masters of crafts. Their work was subject to extremely strict regulation and control by the council. City employees, labourers, and journeymen, most of whom were not citizens, constituted a further group. Together with the regularly unemployed, they made up a sub-stantial proletariat. There was a highly organized system of poor-relief and, at least according to legislation, no-one ever went hungry. The city, a close-knit community bound together by mutual self-interest, had a political and social system that regarded nothing as irrelevant to the public purpose. Owing to this particular structure the Reformation there took a unique form. Religious reform occurred without any of the social or political unrest that characterized the Reformation in so many other cities of Germany and Switzerland (Seebass).

The Reformation, begun by Martin Luther in 1517, was initially a popular movement in Germany. Luther himself came to Nuremberg in 1518, and his teachings were already firmly established there among the populace as early as 1523. Lutheranism appeared to many ordinary citi-zens in Nuremberg as a liberating gospel of faith and confidence. It was also attractive to members of the city's ruling classes. The patricians had no particular love for the authority of Rome in ecclesiastical matters, and welcomed an opportunity to strengthen the city's control over its own religious affairs.

Lutheranism was peacefully adopted as the official state religion in 1525, since it was generally agreed that there could only be one faith preached in the city. Monasteries, nunneries and other religious establishments were suppressed, and their wealth and privileges passed into the control of the city. Such action was far from radical. In this particular instance, popular sentiment coincided with the interests of the ruling classes. Lutheranism was a faith which supported the status quo and crushed any radical efforts to establish spiritual or political independence for the mass of the population. The spiritual values of Lutheranism accorded perfectly with, and gave theological support to, the conservative authoritarianism of the Nuremberg patricians (fig. 38).

This was the extent to which the city was prepared to stand against the interests of the Catholic emperor. During the struggles in the following decades between the Protestant alliance of princes and cities on the one hand and the emperor and the Catholic league on the other, Nuremberg refused to take direct action as long as possible. It was the only Protes-tant city not to join the Schmalkaldic league of 1535.

As political and religious affairs in Germany became increasingly inter-dependent, Nuremberg's attempt to maintain a neutral stance in these matters led to a loss of the city's political momentum. Thus Nuremberg, although avoiding the hardships of defeat in the conflicts of the time, was deprived of the spoils of success. Ironically, this appears to have been beneficial at first, since it made the city into a sedate and undisturbed venue for trading. Yet the progressive marginalization of Nuremberg's politi-cal position eventually also had a detrimental effect on the city's trade and manufacture.

38 Baptism of Christ against a backdrop of Nuremberg from the east, with Reformers kneeling in the foreground
Anonymous engraving, 1630, similar to an engraving of 1559 attributed to the school of Cranach (Smith, 35).
BL, Maps 28840 (14).

Trade routes and commerce

Nuremberg's trade network was established during the middle ages and gradually extended as the city itself became more powerful (Müller). In 1332 tax exemptions were granted for its trade with seventy-two different localities. During the fifteenth century, the south German cities gradually cut in on transactions formerly monopolized by the Hanseatic cities of Hamburg, Lübeck and Bremen. Unlike Ulm, Strasbourg, and Augsburg, Nuremberg already had a tradition of placing merchants in Italy, Flanders and Brabant in large numbers (fig. 39). In addition,

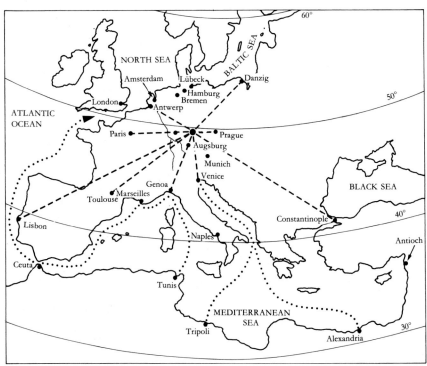

39 Nuremberg as a trading centre
The city lay on a number of major trading routes between the Mediterranean and the Baltic, Spain and eastern Europe. Latitudes 30°, 40°, 50° and 60° are indicated.

Item die drey Symbola Oder Bekanntnus dess reinen wahren Christlichen glaubens welchen der Teuffel mit seinen glydern von anfang heer biß auff den heütigen Tag verfolgt. Einem iederen Christen gar notig zu wissen vnd alle augenblick zu betrachten

favourable treatment was accorded to foreign merchants who wished to live and trade in the city.

Merchants of Nuremberg used a system of *Gesellschaften* or associateships, a characteristic trading organization which consisted of blood relatives working as factors in each foreign city. Around 1500 there were two hundred and thirty-two Nuremberg merchants in Venice, compared with five from Strasbourg and sixty-two from Augsburg (fig. 40). There were also reciprocal customs treaties concluded with many other important European cities. Routes to all these destinations were controlled and exactly described in the Nuremberg *Geleitbuch*, or 'Escort Manual' (Strauss, 127–33).

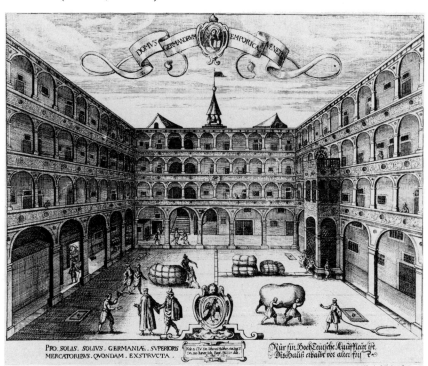

40 Merchants of Upper Germany in the German Emporium at Venice *Engraving by Raphael Cristov, 1616.* GNM, HB 2300.

The traffic of the Nuremberg merchants consisted primarily of safe commodities and staples. They imported materials such as silk from southern France, cotton from Egypt and saffron and fruit from the Levant, and exported high quality manufactured goods of glass, metal, leather, paper and clay. Lorenz Meder's *Handel Buch* of 1558 shows his business embraced Lisbon, Lyons, Antwerp, Cracow and Warsaw, and was linked to all parts of the globe (fig. 41; Kellenbenz I; Braudel, 188–9). In the 1520s two Nuremberg merchants, Jakob Cromberger and Lazarus Nürnberger, were among the first non-Castilians to become involved in Caribbean trading (Strauss, 129–30). Most of their compatriots, however, found such activities too adventurous.

The expansion of overland trade in the late fifteenth and early sixteenth centuries favoured Nuremberg which lay on a number of routes between the Mediterranean and the Baltic, Spain and the Hapsburg territories in the east. In the long term, the discovery of the New World completely upset established trade patterns. Venice and Genoa lost their central role as naval powers, and the chief entrepôt became first Antwerp and subsequently Amsterdam. All the south German cities were eventually adversely affected by this change. Around 1500, however, Nuremberg seemed to be in a position to benefit from the buoyant trade and demand for its manufactured goods, particularly metal ware. There were three trade fairs held annually in Nuremberg, at New Year, Easter, and St. Egidius (September 1), each one lasting for three weeks. During these periods traders from all over Europe came to buy Nuremberg products.

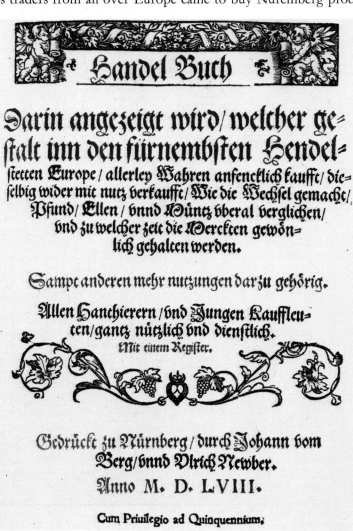

41 Title page from Lorenz Meder, *Handel Buch* (Nuremberg, 1558) BSB, Rar. 2083 (2).

Crafts and manufacture

The development of Nuremberg's commerce was paralleled by the increasingly varied and specialized handicrafts practised there. A relatively large proportion of Nuremberg's population was involved in the specialized manufacture of all kinds of goods (fig. 42). The liberal trade policy of the city encouraged the diversification of the design and production of native products. Nuremberg's artisans were fortunate to have raw materials from the whole world at their disposal, as well as an international market for their wares. Owing to this large market, the craftsmen were in a position to become specialists, highly trained individuals whose range of products was both limited and protected by strict council legislation. This legislation was also intended to protect technological secrets from outside competitors. Those of the metal industries were rigidly enforced.

Reflecting this concern with secrecy, there were basically two types of craft in Nuremberg, *Geschworne Handwerke* (sworn crafts) and *Freie Künste* (free crafts). In practice there was a third group which fell between the two, which suggests that the distinction was less rigid than the statutes imply (Pilz I, 8–9). The most important sworn crafts were those which used metal, such as the goldsmiths and coppersmiths. Members of the sworn crafts had to be citizens and were only allowed to travel with permission from the city council. Nuremberg was not the only place where such draconian policies were adopted. The main difference between the craft system in Nuremberg and that found in other German towns was that it was centrally controlled. Otherwise the structure of the system was much the same. Regulations were made for each craft concerning the training of apprentices, the appointment of masters, quality control, and so on. All craft statutes were entered in the 'Book of Handicrafts' in 1535, to which amendments were periodically added.

Der Vhrmacher.

Ich mache die reysenden Vhr/
Gerecht vnd Glatt nach der Mensur/
Von hellem glaß vnd kleim Vhrsant/
Gut/daß sie haben langen bestandt/
Mach auch darzu Hültzen Geheuß/
Dareyn ich sie fleissig beschleuß/
Ferb die gheuß Grün/Graw/rot vñ blaw
Drinn man die Stund vnd vierteil hab.

S iij   Der

Der Circkelschmidt.

Ich mach mancherley Werckzeug art/
Subtile Zirckel vnd Daßart/
Mancherley Zangen / gschraufft vñ glatt/
Dreh Eyßn/Gärb Eyßn/in vil Werckstat/
Dem holtzdrechßl/rotschmidt vñ schreiner/
Kandelgiesser vnd Balbierer/
Mach auch künstlicher Stück sehr viel/
Rein gegraben/glatt vnd subtil.

X ij   Der

42 The Clockmaker and the Divider-smith
Hans Sachs and Jost Amman, Eygentliche Beschreibung aller Stände auff Erden *(Frankfurt, 1568).*

Nuremberg's reputation as a manufacturing centre was based especially on its metal goods, which were unmatched for their quality throughout Europe. While the materials used for these ranged from gold and silver to iron, brass was particularly favoured. The bronze and brass workers formed one of the oldest and most important sworn crafts of the city. Techniques for the production of bronze, and later brass, were closely-guarded secrets. The copper, tin and zinc ore necessary for their production were supplied by wholesalers of Nuremberg, Augsburg and Leipzig from mines in the Harz, the Upper Palatinate and the Black Forest. Armaments, bells, trumpets and domestic hardware were among the earliest wares made in brass (Dettling; Wörthmüller).

By the middle of the fifteenth century, production of scientific instruments had apparently started in Nuremberg. In 1444 Cardinal Nicholas of Cusa was in the city as the representative of the Pope at the Imperial Diet. While he was there, he took the opportunity to buy three astronomical instruments (a torquetum, an astrolabe and a globe) and sixteen books. The instruments still survive today at Bernkastel-Cues. It seems that they were made by brass workers under the direction of Nicholas Heybech who was living in Nuremberg at the time (Hartmann; Zinner I, 286–7).

This example only indicates that at first specialized instruments were designed and constructed by academics and astronomers who commissioned prefabricated parts to be made by craftsmen. Gradually the production of certain types of standard instruments, such as the diptych dial, was taken on and organized by artisan-astronomers and artisans themselves. The emergence of the compass-makers is evidence of this process. Their craft was obviously already in the 1480s distinguished from that of the divider-smiths; dividers, somewhat confusingly, are also known as compasses from the Latin term *compassum*. In Nuremberg documents written in German, a distinction is consistently made between *Kompassmacher* and *Zirkelschmied*. This, however, does not preclude the possibility that some of the established divider-smiths applied themselves to the new, perhaps fashionable craft of *Kompassmacher* while it remained a free craft.

The development of Nuremberg's commerce and trade enabled the cultural and intellectual life of the city to flourish. Printing presses were first set up there in the 1470s, and it soon became a major centre for the production of woodcuts and copper engravings of both a technical and artistic nature (Clair, 30–3). The presence of these skilled craftsmen, together with the political and commercial attractions of Nuremberg, acted as a powerful lure to the astronomer Johann Müller of Königsberg, better known as Regiomontanus (1436–1476). He settled in Nuremberg in 1471 and set up both a workshop and printing press for the production of scientific instruments and books. During the next five years he contributed vastly to Nuremberg's reputation as a centre for mathematical and astronomical studies in Germany (Zinner III, 163–236). The artistic and technical context within which instruments such as the diptych dial were successfully introduced and developed as a commercial proposition is considered in Chapter six.

The seventeenth century

The peak of Nuremberg's artistic fame was reached in the first decades of the sixteenth century, which coincided with the city's most wealthy and peaceful era. The many paintings, prints and drawings produced by Albrecht Dürer (1471–1528) epitomize the quality and influence of Nuremberg art at the time. As we have already seen, in 1525 the city became

43 Journey and mileage table, by George Kreydlein, Nuremberg, 1560
The table, oriented south-north, indicates the towns between Nuremberg and thirteen major German cities on different routes.
GNM, HB 23191.

involved in various religious and political struggles which lasted until the 1550s. There then followed some decades of relative stability.

It was towards the end of the sixteenth century that William Smith (1550–1618), an English businessman and traveller, came to live in Nuremberg for more than a decade until his departure in 1591. A member of the Haberdashers' Company in London, Smith was also keenly interested in cartography and heraldry. His 'Description of the Cittie of Noremberg' (1594) not only offers an account of its architectural, political and social structure. It also includes a map of the territory, a map and view of the city and several pages of armorial devices of the patrician families (Plate XVII). Smith was of the opinion that 'there is not a cittie in the world, where the people are more civil', and remarked on how it was 'replenished with cunning artificers of fyne workes, which are carried into all places of the world' (Roach, 206, 216). Smith's enthusiastic account must remind us that even at the very end of the sixteenth century Nuremberg's decline was far from being apparent to contemporaries, nor was it inevitable.

A real blow to Nuremberg's fortunes, however, was the conflict known as the Thirty Years' War. During the years between 1618 and 1648 Germany became an international battlefield, as well as being subject to famine and plague. Although Nuremberg never suffered the ravages and bloodshed experienced in some other places, the war sapped the city's financial and cultural resources to such an extent that it never recovered its former prominence as a city state. In the international context, Germany as a whole suffered severe economic and political decline in the

44 'Gesellenstechen' at the
Hauptmarkt, Nuremberg, on
3 March 1561
*Painting by Jost Amman showing
jousting of patrician families.*
BNM.

seventeenth century.   In contrast, countries such as the Netherlands and
England were becoming relatively prosperous by the second half of the
century.

It is against this background that the changing fortunes of the compass-
makers can be traced.   The conditions which fostered innovation and
development in the early sixteenth century were no longer present by the
end of the seventeenth century.   As will be shown in the following
chapters, the heyday of the ivory compass-makers appears to have been
during the period between about 1580 and 1610.   After the middle of the
seventeenth century few large diptychs of high quality seem to have been
produced, and there was relatively more emphasis on the manufacture of
small and functional pieces.

CHAPTER FOUR

Who made them?

The Nuremberg ivory diptych dials, which survive today because of their durability, provide a marvellous starting-point for a study of their makers (fig. 45). This is because on many of these instruments there is one or more of the following pieces of information: the maker's full name or initials; an identifying mark; the date of production; the mark 'N' or 'Nuremberg'. A brief survey of these details immediately reveals that, with relatively few exceptions, these surviving dials were all made by members of six families during a period between around 1550 and 1700. The dominant families were: KARNER, LESEL, MILLER, REINMANN, TROSCHEL, TUCHER.

There are a few instruments signed by other individuals. Examples by Johann Gebhart (figs 46, 78), Christian Heiden (fig. 93) and Georg Hartmann (Plate II, figs 14, 72) are found in this exhibition. At present, only three other names have been found on dated ivory diptychs from Nuremberg: Linhart Gresel (1531; Science Museum, London), Hans Felt (1566; Aachen) and Georg Riege (1699; Aachen) (Zinner I, 326, 314, 491). Felt, Gresel, Gebhart and Riege all seem to have been craft members, but the relationship of Heiden and Hartmann to the compass-makers is ambivalent. One other compass-maker whose importance will become apparent was Erhard Etzlaub (fl. 1484–1532), although there are no known ivory diptychs by him.

45 Kompassmacher, 1549
Hausbuch der Mendelschen Zwölfbrüderstiftung II, fol. 1ᵛ.
Nuremberg, Stadtbibliothek.
Photograph by Foto Hilbinger
GmbH, Schwaig-Behringersdorf.

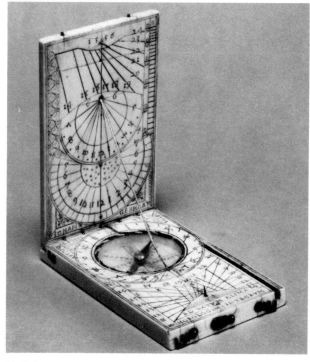

46 Johann Gebhart, 1556 Cat. 54. *(Compare figs 52 and 78).*

The biographical information that can be gleaned from the instruments alone is important, if limited.   It is, after all, the instruments themselves which have alerted us to the existence of the Nuremberg compass-makers in the first place.   If we wish to know more about the people who made them, however, other historical methods have to be employed.

Archival sources

It is fortunate that in the Nuremberg archives today there is a great deal of documentary material which can be used to provide genealogical and biographical details about the compass-makers.   These archives include the Nuremberg *Stadtarchiv* (NSA), the Nuremberg *Staatsarchiv* (NStA) and the *Landeskirchliches Archiv* of Nuremberg (LKA).   The LKA contains parish records which were introduced in Nuremberg with the Protestant Reformation of the 1520s.   Most baptisms, marriages, deaths and burials in the two city parishes of St. Lorenz and St. Sebald were thus registered in the period when the compass-makers flourished.   To this basic genea-logical information can be added details from a range of legal and financial records of the courts.   These include, for example, the *Libri Litt.* or *Grundverbriefungsbücher,* books recording dealings of securities on land (now in the NSA), and the *Inventarbücher* or inventory books (also kept in the NSA).   Such documents provide details of houses bought and sold, debts incurred, guardians appointed, and hints of family squabbles and legal wrangles over inheritances.   Another source, of which selec-tions are published, are the *Ratsverlässe,* the proceedings of the city council (Hampe; the full manuscript is in the NStA).

In using such material, however, considerable caution has to be exer-cised.   It is tempting to make unproven assumptions and to draw hasty conclusions.   For example, members of a single family who all had the same Christian name are easily confused.   Hans (usually given to the first-born son) and Georg were particularly popular names.   An addi-tional complication arises where the family name was quite common, as in the case of the name Miller, for example.

Original research has been undertaken into the Karner, Lesel, Rein-mann and Miller families for this study.   The results of researches into the Tuchers and Troschels have already been published (Kühnlein; Chandler & Vincent II).   Unless otherwise stated, information about the Tuchers and Troschels has been taken from these published sources.   The only other compass-maker whose life has been studied in similar detail is Erhard Etzlaub (Schnelbögl I & II).

The principal familes

From all this material, charts illustrating the family connections of compass-makers in four of the six families – Karner, Lesel, Tucher, Troschel – have been drawn up, complemented with lists for the Rein-mann and Miller families (Tables 1–5).   For reasons of clarity, details of spouses and children who were not known to have been compass-makers have been omitted.   Since these tables are intended to provide a reference guide to the principal makers of ivory diptychs, the marks and stylistic features characteristic of these makers are indicated in abbreviated form.   The most common marks on the ivory diptychs are depicted together in figure 104.   Where information about a house is known, the street name and date of the reference has been included.   This data has been correlated with an eighteenth-century map of Nuremberg which provides a graphic representation of the major distribution of compass-making families (fig. 47).   It is immediately clear from the map that most

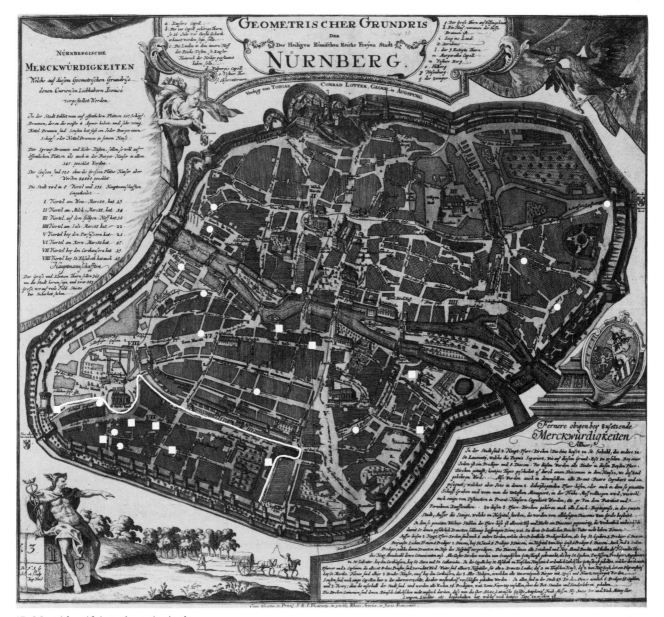

47 Map identifying the principal locations of compass-makers in Nuremberg
Based on a map by Tobias Conrad Lotter, c. 1733.
NSA, A 3 Pläne 378.

● = 1 reference
■ = more than one reference.

of them lived in the parish of St. Lorenz (south of the river Pegnitz), and within this area they were concentrated in the so-called Carthusian quarter, the south-west part of the city. More detailed observations about each of the six families, the instruments their members made and the marks they used, are made below.

Other compass-makers

Apart from establishing the genealogies of the main families, it has also been possible to draw up a provisional list of other known compass-makers, and (less successfully) of where they lived (Table 6). The most important sources for these names are in two volumes of council records. The first of these (NStA, *Amts- u. Standbücher* Rep. 52 b, vol. 305) lists the names of those who became *Bürger* (citizens) of the city and their professions during the 1480s and 90s. The second (NStA, *Amts- u. Standbücher* Rep. 52 b, vol. 309, fol. 14) consists of a list of names of those who were made masters of the compass-makers between 1537 and 1570. Other references to compass-makers have been found in the *Libri Litt.* and *Inventarbücher* (NSA). A further source, not yet mentioned, is the *Compaszmacher Schuldtbuch,* the debt book of the compass-makers between 1674 and 1715 (NSA).   The surprising number of references yielded from these records would suggest that the surviving instruments represent only a fraction of those made in Nuremberg during the sixteenth and seventeenth centuries.

The archival research into the Nuremberg compass-makers is far from complete.   Apart from the articles already mentioned, two published works have also been used as sources for names of compass-makers (Werner; Zinner I).   These names have been included in the table, but since no documentation is provided in the above-mentioned publications, they can only be regarded as provisional until checked further in the archives.

The principal compass-makers

One of the most striking results of the study is that there were many more compass-makers in the Karner, Tucher, Reinmann and Miller families than are indicated by surviving ivory diptychs.   Unless it is assumed that these instruments are not a representative sample, one conclusion to be drawn is that some members of these families confined themselves to the production of wooden instruments.   Another possibility is that while an individual might be described as a compass-maker, he worked for another family member, or even an outside commissioner, who actually signed the instruments.   The case of the Karners amply illustrates the kind of question raised here.

Karner and Lesel families

Since it has been possible to establish a relatively complete genealogy for the Karners, the family and its connections can be presented in some detail (Table 1).   There are five discernable generations of compass-makers in the Karner dynasty.   No instruments survive from the makers of the first generation.   The first of these was Caspar (fl. 1564–c. 1585).   Between 1565 and 1585 he and his wife Elisabeth had eight children.   In 1590 Elisabeth, by then a widow, married the compass-maker Albrecht Lösel or Lesel (fl. 1590–1610); they had a son Michael (1591–fl. 1629).   An ivory diptych by Albrecht dated 1610 survives.   Michael was also a compass-maker who made ivory diptychs dated between around 1613 and 1629; these are stamped with a crown (Zinner I, 427, 429).   Why he should have adopted the Reinmann crown mark is not yet known; perhaps he worked in the Reinmann workshop or was related to the family by marriage.

Roughly contemporary with Caspar was the compass-maker Conrad I (fl. 1567–1571).   The identity of his parents and the date of his birth have not yet been established.   It might be conjectured that he and Caspar were brothers, but there is no supporting evidence.   Fortunately, after this point, the documentation improves.   The family is divided into two branches, one descending from Hans 'the elder', the other from Conrad II, who was the son of Conrad I.   Since members of this latter branch were those who are known to have made ivory diptychs, they will be considered first.

Conrad II (1571–1632) used a hunting horn as his mark (fig. 48; Zinner I, 401–2).   Four of his eight sons were compass-makers.   For two of them, Martin (1606–fl. 1632) and Erasmus (1614–1651), we have no evidence of surviving works.   A third son, Jacob (1612–fl. 1648) used the mark '3' or 'J3K' to sign his ivory diptychs (fig. 16; Zinner I, 402–3).   Jacob himself had seven children; his eldest surviving son, Jacob Friedrich (1640–1686), was also a compass-maker, but no examples of his

48 Conrad Karner, before 1632
Cat. 8.

work are known. The last son of Conrad II, Albrecht (1619–1687), modified his father's mark of a hunting horn for use on his own diptychs (Zinner I, 400–1). Zinner refers to a signed and dated instrument of an Albrecht Karner of 1688; yet the parish records state that our Albrecht was buried on August 21 1687. Thus one might assume that either Albrecht's workshop continued to use his name, or that another yet unidentified compass-maker Albrecht Karner was responsible for this diptych. Elisabeth gave Albrecht eleven children between 1642 and 1660. Three of these became compass-makers: Melchior, Georg and Hans. Albrecht and these three sons were professional violinists as well as compass-makers.

Melchior (1642–1707) was the eldest of the three. His instruments can sometimes be identified by the mark '4' (Zinner I, 403–4), presumably following on from his uncle's mark '3'. Melchior's workshop was probably responsible for at least some of the very small unmarked ivory-and-wood or bone-and-wood dials which were produced in the latter part of the seventeenth century (fig. 49). His brother Georg (1648–fl. 1688) who used the sign of a right-facing prancing horse on his instruments (fig.

49 Probably Karner workshop; late 17th/early 18th century
Upper leaf bone, lower leaf bone with wooden core.
Cat. 58.

TABLE 1: Karner and Lesel families

LESEL FAMILY   KARNER FAMILY

Albrecht
ⓞ   22.6.1590
ivory diptych 1610

Elisabeth
ⓞ   I Caspar Karner
ⓞ   II Albrecht Lesel

Caspar
*   1542?
ⓞ   17.4.1564
ℳ   5.5.1564
†   after 1585, before 1590
℘   Schottengasse 1579

Michael
*   22.3.1591
crown mark (10) 1612–29
scrollwork: flowers, fruit, animals
Cat. 11

Hans I
ⓞ   1.7.1588
†   10.8.1632
℘   Kühnertsgasse before 1610
℘   Am Katharinen Kloster sold property 1612
℘   Kartäusergasse 1615

Hans II
*   28.2.1597
ⓞ   25.8.1618
ⓞ   27.4.1646
ⓞ   19.9.1676
℘   Am Katharinen Kloster sold property 1634
℘   Kartäusergasse 1645–74
marriage organizer; landlord

Andreas
*   12.12.1620
ⓞ   15.3.1642
†   4.7.1682
℘   Kühnertsgasse 1682

Hans Paulus
*   28.4.1606
†   26.9.1627
℘   Maiengasse 1626

Key:
Name in bold = maker of ivory diptychs
  * = born or baptized
  ℳ = made master
   ⓞ = married
  † = died or buried
  ℘ = property or lodgings

Details of instruments, mark and identifying
features are shown in *italic* with catalogue
numbers in **bold**

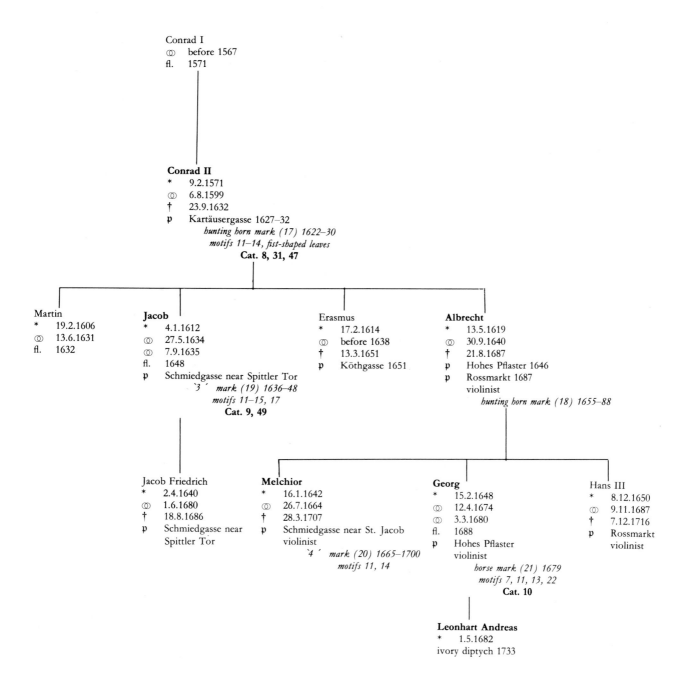

Conrad I
Ⓞ before 1567
fl.   1571

Conrad II
*   9.2.1571
Ⓞ 6.8.1599
† 23.9.1632
℗ Kartäusergasse 1627–32
      hunting horn mark (17) 1622–30
      motifs 11–14, fist-shaped leaves
Cat. 8, 31, 47

Martin
*   19.2.1606
Ⓞ 13.6.1631
fl. 1632

Jacob
*   4.1.1612
Ⓞ 27.5.1634
Ⓞ 7.9.1635
fl. 1648
℗ Schmiedgasse near Spittler Tor
      `3´ mark (19) 1636–48
      motifs 11–15, 17
Cat. 9, 49

Erasmus
*   17.2.1614
Ⓞ before 1638
† 13.3.1651
℗ Köthgasse 1651

Albrecht
*   13.5.1619
Ⓞ 30.9.1640
† 21.8.1687
℗ Hohes Pflaster 1646
℗ Rossmarkt 1687
   violinist
      hunting horn mark (18) 1655–88

Jacob Friedrich
*   2.4.1640
Ⓞ 1.6.1680
† 18.8.1686
℗ Schmiedgasse near
   Spittler Tor

Melchior
*   16.1.1642
Ⓞ 26.7.1664
† 28.3.1707
℗ Schmiedgasse near St. Jacob
   violinist
      `4´ mark (20) 1665–1700
      motifs 11, 14

Georg
*   15.2.1648
Ⓞ 12.4.1674
Ⓞ 3.3.1680
fl. 1688
℗ Hohes Pflaster
   violinist
      horse mark (21) 1679
      motifs 7, 11, 13, 22
Cat. 10

Hans III
*   8.12.1650
Ⓞ 9.11.1687
† 7.12.1716
℗ Rossmarkt
   violinist

Leonhart Andreas
*   1.5.1682
ivory diptych 1733

50 Georg Karner, late 17th century. Cat. 10.

50; Zinner I, 402) certainly produced some of the smallest-size diptychs. One of Georg's sons, Leonhard Andreas (1682–fl. 1733), is the last member of the family known to have produced ivory instruments; a single example of his work dated 1733 survives in the National Maritime Museum, Greenwich (Zinner I, 403). The third of the compass-maker-violinist brothers was Hans (1650–1716). No instruments by Hans are known, but it may be that he worked anonymously in a family workshop or else used a mark which has not yet been identified with a particular maker. One such mark on the small-size diptychs of this period is the hand (Cat. 46; fig. 104, mark 22).

The second, previously unknown, branch of the family begins with Hans 'the elder' (fl. 1588–d. 1632). It is possible that he was either the son of Caspar or of Conrad I. Hans I had two sons, and both became compass-makers. The younger of the two, Hans Paulus (1606–1627), died at the age of 21. In contrast, the first-born son, confusingly known as Hans 'the younger' (1597–1681), had a long and eventful life. From his first marriage he had six sons, of whom only the second, Andreas (1620–1682) has been identified as a compass-maker. Like members of the first family branch, Hans II combined the craft of compass-maker with other trades. In 1642 he was described as a *Hochzeitlader* (professional marriage organizer). Between 1650 and 1675 he was both a landlord and victualler in the Kartäusergasse, which seems to have been in the same place as his workshop.

Tucher (Ducher) family

Attempts at establishing the precise lineage of the earliest compass-makers in the Tucher family have so far met with failure. Kühnlein has suggested that Jörg (fl. 1490–1496) was Hans I's father, but this is pure conjecture (see Table 2). Katherina Tucher (fl. 1530), a female compass-maker, could have been the widow or daughter of Jörg or another

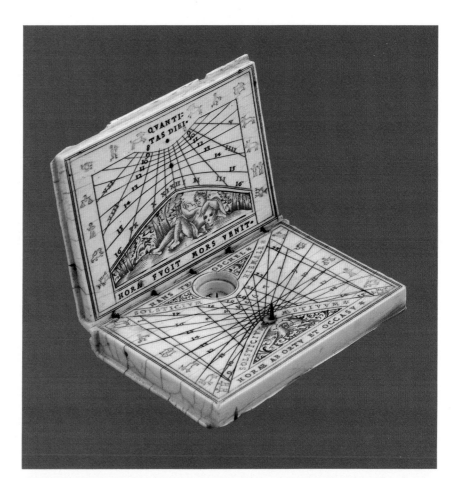

PLATE I: Hans Troschel, 1b/2a
Cat. 33.

PLATE II: Georg Hartmann, 1562,
1b/2a
Cat. 24.

PLATE III: Leonhart Miller, 1613,
1b/2a
Cat. 38.

PLATE IV: Paul Reinmann, c. 1600,
1b/2a
Cat. 42.

PLATE V: Thomas Tucher, 1a
Cat. 41.

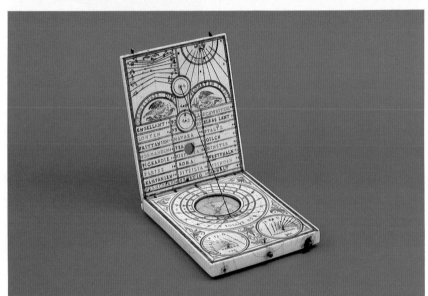

PLATE VI: Thomas Tucher, 1b/2a
Cat. 3.

PLATE VII: Thomas Tucher, 1b/2a
Cat. 36.

PLATE VIII: Hans Tucher, 1588,
1b/2a
Cat. 27.

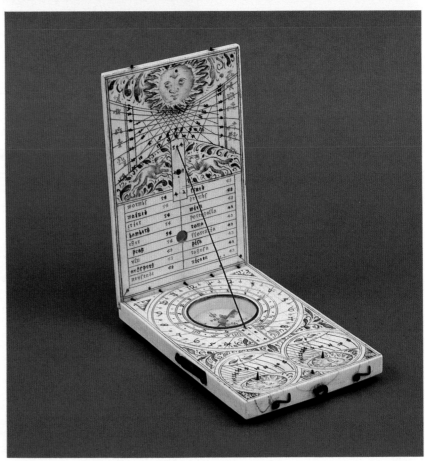

PLATE IX: Joseph Tucher, 1b/2a
Cat. 40.

TABLE 2: Tucher family

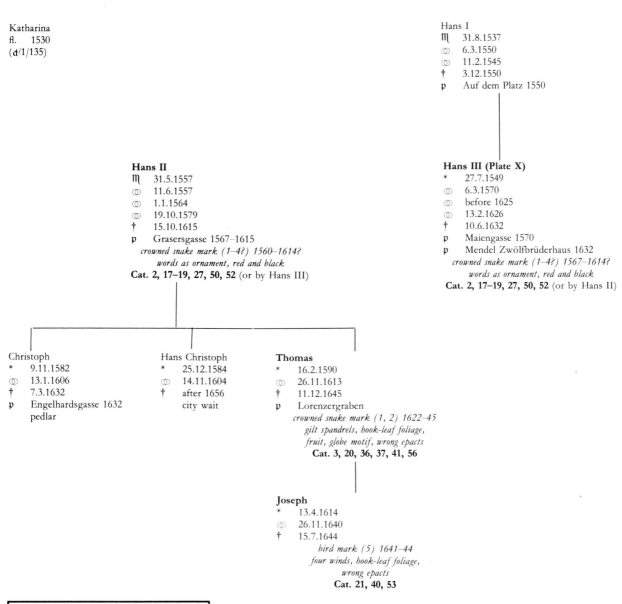

Jörg
fl. 1492–96

Katharina
fl. 1530
(₫/1/135)

Hans I
Ⓜ 31.8.1537
Ⓒ 6.3.1550
Ⓒ 11.2.1545
† 3.12.1550
℗ Auf dem Platz 1550

Hans II
Ⓜ 31.5.1557
Ⓒ 11.6.1557
Ⓒ 1.1.1564
Ⓒ 19.10.1579
† 15.10.1615
℗ Grasersgasse 1567–1615
crowned snake mark (1–4?) 1560–1614?
words as ornament, red and black
Cat. 2, 17–19, 27, 50, 52 (or by Hans III)

Hans III (Plate X)
* 27.7.1549
Ⓒ 6.3.1570
Ⓒ before 1625
Ⓒ 13.2.1626
† 10.6.1632
℗ Maiengasse 1570
℗ Mendel Zwölfbrüderhaus 1632
crowned snake mark (1–4?) 1567–1614?
words as ornament, red and black
Cat. 2, 17–19, 27, 50, 52 (or by Hans II)

Christoph
* 9.11.1582
Ⓒ 13.1.1606
† 7.3.1632
℗ Engelhardsgasse 1632
pedlar

Hans Christoph
* 25.12.1584
Ⓒ 14.11.1604
† after 1656
city wait

Thomas
* 16.2.1590
Ⓒ 26.11.1613
† 11.12.1645
℗ Lorenzergraben
crowned snake mark (1, 2) 1622–45
gilt spandrels, hook-leaf foliage,
fruit, globe motif, wrong epacts
Cat. 3, 20, 36, 37, 41, 56

Joseph
* 13.4.1614
Ⓒ 26.11.1640
† 15.7.1644
bird mark (5) 1641–44
four winds, hook-leaf foliage,
wrong epacts
Cat. 21, 40, 53

Key:
Name in bold = maker of ivory diptychs
* = born or baptized
Ⓜ = made master
Ⓒ = married
† = died or buried
℗ = property or lodgings
₫ = NSA, *Inventarbücher des*
 Stadtgerichts Rep. B.14.

Details of instruments, mark and identifying
features are shown in *italic* with catalogue
numbers in **bold**

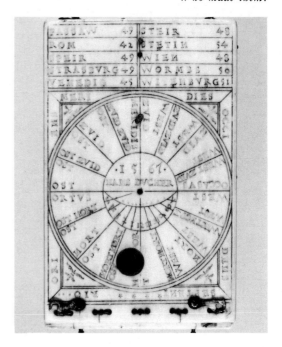

51 Hans Tucher, 1567
leaf 1a.
Cat. 17.

unknown family member.   It is also impossible to establish the correspondence between the three Hans Tuchers (who became masters in 1537,
1557 and 1570 respectively) and the instruments made by makers of the
same name.   Hans I died in 1550, and thus it can safely be assumed that
he did not make any of the dated ivory diptychs of 1560–1614 (fig. 51;
Zinner I, 556–60); these could have been made either by Hans II
(fl. 1557–1631) or Hans III (1549–1632).   There are no fewer than four
different snake marks on Tucher dials.

Hans II's son Thomas (1590–1645) used two of these snake marks
between about 1620 and 1645.   Zinner's attribution of all instruments
with snake mark and initials 'TD' to this Thomas Tucher is questionable
(Zinner I, 563–7).   At first it might be thought difficult to determine the
maker of any unsigned diptych punched with a snake.   Yet as is shown
in more detail in Chapter six, it should be possible to distinguish between
instruments by the Hans Tuchers and those of Thomas on both ornamental and technical grounds.   Thomas's son Joseph (1614–1644) abandoned
the snake mark and used a bird flying to the left instead (Zinner I, 563).

Hans III, apparently known as 'the elder', ended his days in the Mendel
Zwölfbrüderhaus.   This was a charitable institution established in 1388 by
Konrad Mendel, which was situated near St. Katherine's cloister.   In
exchange for an entrance fee and a transfer of property, twelve elderly
craftsmen at any one time had the right to food and lodging for life.   The
likeness of each 'brother', together with the tools of his craft, was always
painted and kept in the *Hausbuch*.   The inscription above the portrait of
Hans III (Plate X) describes him as a compass-maker and *Züngleinrichter*
(compass-needle maker?) who entered the institution in September 1631
at the age of 84 and died the following June (M. Wagner I, 46; M. Wagner
II, 64).

Of the three compass-maker sons of Hans II, only the youngest,
Thomas, apparently made ivory instruments.   His two elder brothers
diversified into different trades.   Christoph (1582–1632) was a *Händler*
(pedlar) by 1628, and Hans Christoph (1584–fl. 1656) was already a *Türmer*
(city wait) by 1625.   (Waits were originally appointed as night watchmen
to guard city boundaries and to act as keepers of the peace.   As a second-
ary duty they played wind-instruments to mark the hours of the day and
night.)

Troschel (Droschel) family

The article by Vincent and Chandler has conclusively demonstrated that there were at least two members of this family who were compass-makers (cf. Zinner I, 551–5, who is less explicit on this point).   The first of these was Hans Troschel the elder (fl. 1578–1612), who used the mark of a thrush on a twig, of which two versions are shown here.   The second was his son Hans (fl. 1616–1631), who used the mark of a six-pointed star (Table 3).   The only problem is to establish whether the younger Hans did not sometimes also use a thrush mark.   If all the different thrushes are of Hans the elder, why did he change his mark? Further investigation is required into the Troschel family and its members.

Reinmann family

It is impossible to establish a proper family tree for the Reinmanns (Table 4).   What has become clear from archival research is that Zinner mistakenly assumed that there was only one Georg Reinmann who made both wooden and ivory instruments between 1531 and 1566 (Zinner I, 481–2).   In fact there were at least three makers of this name, two of them working at the same period.   Which of them made the ivory diptychs is not known.   A similar problem is encountered when trying to identify the three compass-makers of this family called Hans.

It can be suggested that Paul Reinmann (1557?–1609), the most prominent ivory compass-maker at the beginning of the seventeenth century, was the son of Hieronymus (fl. 1556–1577).   The fact that both of these makers used a crown for their mark lends weight to this argument. Hieronymus was himself a successful maker of ivory diptychs whose work was known to the emperor (fig. 52; Zinner I, 484–5).   At his death, his inventory was worth 218 guilders.   The quality of the instruments made by Paul, many of which are finely engraved and have gilt brass fittings, reinforces the impression that he was a wealthy craftsman who could afford the best materials and workmanship for his diptychs.   It is possible that Paul was also a brass-smith, since there are a number of examples of gunner's levels and even sundials made in gilt brass that are signed by him or stamped with his crown mark (Zinner I, 485–90).

52 Hieronymus Reinmann, 1559
leaf 1a. Compare the sun-face in Plate II.
The overall design is also similar to one
favoured by Johann Gebhart; see figs 46
and 78.
Cat. 22.

TABLE 3: Troschel family

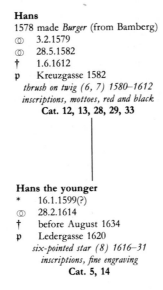

Hans
1578 made *Burger* (from Bamberg)
⓪   3.2.1579
⓪   28.5.1582
†   1.6.1612
℗   Kreuzgasse 1582
      thrush on twig (6, 7) 1580–1612
      inscriptions, mottoes, red and black
            Cat. 12, 13, 28, 29, 33

Hans the younger
*   16.1.1599(?)
⓪   28.2.1614
†   before August 1634
℗   Ledergasse 1620
      six-pointed star (8) 1616–31
      inscriptions, fine engraving
            Cat. 5, 14

TABLE 4: Reinmann family (In approximate chronological order)

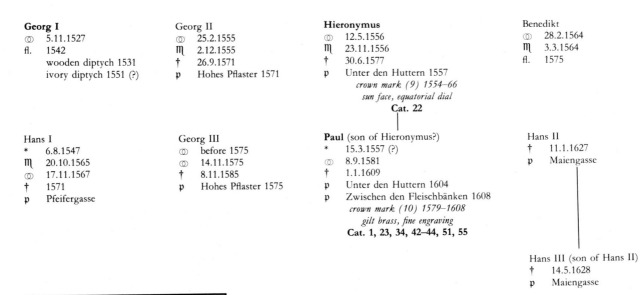

Georg I
⓪   5.11.1527
fl.   1542
      wooden diptych 1531
      ivory diptych 1551 (?)

Georg II
⓪   25.2.1555
ℳ   2.12.1555
†   26.9.1571
℗   Hohes Pflaster 1571

Hieronymus
⓪   12.5.1556
ℳ   23.11.1556
†   30.6.1577
℗   Unter den Huttern 1557
      crown mark (9) 1554–66
      sun face, equatorial dial
          Cat. 22

Benedikt
⓪   28.2.1564
ℳ   3.3.1564
fl.   1575

Hans I
*   6.8.1547
ℳ   20.10.1565
⓪   17.11.1567
†   1571
℗   Pfeifergasse

Georg III
⓪   before 1575
⓪   14.11.1575
†   8.11.1585
℗   Hohes Pflaster 1575

Paul (son of Hieronymus?)
*   15.3.1557 (?)
⓪   8.9.1581
†   1.1.1609
℗   Unter den Huttern 1604
℗   Zwischen den Fleischbänken 1608
      crown mark (10) 1579–1608
      gilt brass, fine engraving
    Cat. 1, 23, 34, 42–44, 51, 55

Hans II
†   11.1.1627
℗   Maiengasse

Hans III (son of Hans II)
†   14.5.1628
℗   Maiengasse

Key:
Name in bold = maker of ivory diptychs
      * = born or baptized
     ℳ = made master
     ⓪ = married
      † = died or buried
     ℗ = property or lodgings

Details of instruments, mark and identifying
features are shown in *italic* with catalogue
numbers in **bold**

53 Leonhart Miller, 1613
leaf 2b.
Cat. 15.

Miller (Müller) family

The list of the compass-makers in the Miller family is extremely tentative and provisional (Table 5). The problem arises in distinguishing between individuals with the same names. In 1538 a compass-maker Hans Müller drew up an inventory of the possessions left to him by his two wives, and established that the compass-maker Linhart Gresel was one of the guardians of his children (NSA, *Inventarbücher* vol. 2, fol. 161ᵛ). Was this the same Hans who died in 1555? Again, a compass-maker called Hans Miller married Margaretha, daughter of Hieronymus Reinmann, in 1587, but he might not have been the same Hans who became a master in 1564. Both Michael (d. 1599) and Georg (fl. 1603) were sons of a compass-maker called Hans, yet this does not mean they were necessarily brothers. Finally, there are records of a compass-maker Hans Miller marrying in 1614, 1616, 1618 and 1619. In Table 5 it has been assumed that these are references to a single individual.

The probem recurs with other favoured Christian names in the family. Between 1558 and 1577 there were eleven children with the first name of Lienhart or Leonhart born to fathers called Caspar, Peter, Nicolaus, Jacob, Lienhard and Sebastian Miller or Müller. Leonhart Miller, who seems to have married in 1594 and died in 1653, was the most prolific producer of ivory diptychs in the family during the first half of the seventeenth century (fig. 53; Zinner I, 446–51). Four different versions of his mark, the fleur-de-lys, can be identified. The ornamental vocabulary used on his instruments was also varied. There remains the possibility that there was more than one Leonhart working at the same period.

Leonhart's son, Nicolaus (1615–fl. 1661), used the mark of a crown on his instruments. This crown can be clearly distinguished from that used by Reinmann and Lesel. It should be remembered that the Reinmanns and Millers became related by marriage in the 1580s. Zinner was apparently incorrect to assume that the Nicolaus Miller who made a diptych dated 1605 was the same Nicolaus whose work is dated between 1642 and 1661 (Zinner I, 451–2) and who was also apparently a *Häfner* (pot-and-pan maker or potter). This research has also conclusively demonstrated that members of the Miller family lived and worked in Nuremberg, not Augsburg, as Zinner suggested.

TABLE 5: Miller family (In approximate chronological order)

Hans I
† 10.10.1555
  Auf der Walch

Hans II
Ⅿ 26.5.1564

Caspar
Ⅿ 26.5.1564
  ivory diptych n.d.

Jörg
ⓞ before 1564
ℙ Nägeleingasse 1564
  ivory diptych n.d.

Georg
ⓞ 24.10.1603

Nicolaus
fl. 1605
  ivory diptych 1605

Hans III
ⓞ 4.5.1613
ℙ Weissgerbergasse 1623

Leonhart
ⓞ 13.5.1594
ⓞ 13.9.1596
† 4.2.1653
ℙ Hintere Beckschlagergasse 1637
  fleur-de-lys mark (12–15) 1602–51
  foliage, fruit, sun face
  Cat. 4, 15, 38, 39

Severinus
* 17.7.1598
ⓞ 18.8.1620
† 21.1.1656
  soldier

Hans ?
ivory diptych n.d.
  mark of shield with flower and star

Hans IV
ⓞ 21.11.1614
ⓞ 16.2.1616
ⓞ 18.8.1618
ⓞ 10.11.1619

Nicolaus (son of Leonhart)
* 6.12.1615
ⓞ 26.8.1640
ℙ Pfaffengässlein 1647
  crown mark (11) 1642–61
  lettering, punched motifs
  Cat. 16

Key:	
Name in bold	= maker of ivory diptychs
*	= born or baptized
Ⅿ	= made master
ⓞ	= married
†	= died or buried
ℙ	= property or lodgings

Details of instruments, mark and identifying features are shown in *italic* with catalogue numbers in **bold**

Craft practice and organization

The organization of the compass-makers of Nuremberg can only be understood fully in the broader context of craft practice there. As has already been explained in Chapter three, there were two main groups of crafts. The closed crafts or *Geschwornen Handwerke* each consisted of a group of artisans under the direction of sworn masters, elected by members, but formally given power by the city council. In order to join a sworn craft as an apprentice it was necessary to be a citizen and to accept restrictions on travel outside the city. The closed or sworn crafts included those on which the prosperity of the citizens depended, notably those which produced goods from metals such as brass and gold (fig. 54). In contrast, the free crafts or *Freien Künste* might be practised by individuals without such strict control, and included, among others, artisans such as painters, sculptors and woodcarvers. There was always considerable fluidity between these two groups of crafts.

The changing status of the compass-makers' craft over a period of two centuries offers a good example of this fluidity. Theirs is a story of the gradual emergence of a new trade whose members sought to establish an autonomous craft, protected from encroachment by outsiders. To a large extent they succeeded in their aim, but at the expense of any further innovation or development of the instruments which they produced.

As is shown in Table 6, the earliest use of the term 'compass-maker' as a profession in the city records dates from the mid-1480s. It is likely that portable compass dials and diptychs were first made in small numbers by craftsmen at the instigation of astronomers such as Regiomontanus, who lived in Nuremberg during the period 1471–6. Demand for these instruments soon became sufficient to encourage more people to specialize in their production.

The first recorded step towards organization of the compass-makers was taken in 1535 when their rules were included in the 'Book of Handicrafts' (now kept in the NStA), the first codification of all such rules to be produced. Although compass-making was probably still a free craft, the

Der Anſehliche aus-und Einzug des Ehr-löblichen Roth-gießer handwercks.

54 Procession of Nuremberg *Rotgiesser* (brass founders), late 17th century
Nuremberg, Stadtgeschichtliche Museen.

1535 rules imply that the council had by then already allowed the masters to exercise some control over their work. This impression is reinforced by council deliberation over complaints of compass-makers in July 1524 (Hampe, nos 1457–8). The rules of 1535 include details of the masterpiece, the training of apprentices and journeymen, restrictions on production, distribution of materials, and other regulations pertaining to craft practice. During the course of the sixteenth century, new obligations and restrictions were added, so that by 1608, when a revised version of the rules appeared, it was already effectively a closed craft. These regulations of 1608 are translated into English here for the first time (Table 7); earlier variants and later amendments have been noted where relevant.

TABLE 6: Known Compass-Makers not in the Main Families

Name	*Biographical details*	*References*
ALBRECHT, Andreas	fl. 1625	W, 112
BYNTER, Jorg	'compastmacher' 1485	1/190
CRISTEL, Conrad	'conbastmacher' 1484	1/186
ETZLAUB, Erhard	burger 1484, fl. 1532	Schnelbögl
	℣ Am Laufer Schlagturm	
	wooden diptychs 1511, 1513	
EUDRISCH, Nicolaus	fl. before 1528	W, 112
FELT, Eberhart	† 1600	W, 113
FELT, Hans	ℳ 1564	2; Z, 314
	ivory diptych 1566; *mark of jester's hat*	
FELT, Martin	fl. 1602	W, 112
FELT, Marx	fl. 1602	W, 112
FELT, Wolf	† 1682	W, 113
FRIESSFELDT, Hans	ℳ 1555	2; Z, 316
	brass diptych	
GAILSDORFER, Hans	ℳ 1538	2; 3/58/46
GAILSTÖRFER, Hans	fl. after 1674	4
GAILSTÖRFER, Jacob	fl. after 1674	4
GEBHART, Johann	burger 1538, fl. 1546–48	Z, 319;
	mark 16, 1546–62	3/61/148
	Cat. 25, Cat. 54	
GRESEL, Hans	fl. 1543	3/56/154
GRESEL, Linhart	fl. 1531–47	Z, 326
	ivory diptych 1531	
GRIBNER, Ludwig	'conpastmacher' 1484	1/187
GRUBER, Hans	fl. 1552	Z, 327
HARDER, Johann	fl. 1657	W, 113
[HARTMANN, Georg	1489–1564	Z, W]
	Cat. 24	
[HEIDEN, Christian	1526–76	Z, W]
	Cat. 26	
HIRSCH, Ott	'conpastmacher' 1487	1/197
KESER, Hans	fl. 1528	3/41/137ᵛ
KOLL, Bernhart	ℳ 1569	2
MARSCH, Ulrich	fl. 1528– † before 1543	3/41/137ᵛ
	℣ Sundergäu on the Graben	3/56/154
MENNGER, Hans	ℳ 1567	2
MENNINGER, Hans	ℳ 1542	2
PFISTER, Martin	fl. 1537–42	3/54/172
	℣ Spitzenberg 1542	
PILGRAM, Benedict	fl. 1524	H, no. 1457
PILGRAM, Fritz	† 1543	5/3/54ᵛ
PILGRAM, Hans	ℳ 1544	2
PILGRAM, Sebald	fl. 1530–47	5/1/119
PIRGER, Wolfgang	'campaszmacher' 1485	1/190
RAWBENGEL, Hans	'conpastmacher' 1487	1/197
REICHER, Georg	fl. 1674	4
RIEGE, Georg	fl. 1699	Z, 491
	ivory diptych 1699; *clover leaf mark*	
RÜHER, Hans Carol	fl. after 1674	4
SCHELNSTAINER, Fritz	'campastmacher' 1487	1/196
SCHELTNER, Heintz	† before 1530	5/1/75ᵛ
SCHELTNER, Heinrich	ℳ 1566	2
SCHELTNER, Michael	fl. 1534–38	3/47/92
	℣ Paniersberg 1534	
SCHELTNER, Sebalt	† before 1534	3/45/119
SINGER, Hans	fl. 1548	3/61/249ᵛ
VOLLAND, Lienhardt	fl. 1544	3/57/115
ZEYDLER, Pangratzus	ℳ 1557	2

Key: (see also select bibliography)		
Name in bold = maker of ivory diptychs		1 = NStA, *Amts -u. Standbücher* Rep. 52b, vol. 305
ℳ = made master		2 = NStA, *Amts -u. Standbücher* Rep. 52b, vol. 309, fol. 14
† = died or buried	H = Hampe	3 = NSA, *Libri Litt.* /vol./folio
℣ = property or lodgings	W = Werner	4 = NSA, *Compaszmacher Schuldtbuch*
	Z = Zinner I	5 = NSA, *Inventarbücher des Stadtgerichts* Rep. B. 14. /vol/folio

CHAPTER FIVE

How were they made?

Craft regulations

According to the craft rules, compass dials were to be made in ivory, good quality boxwood, or (from 1608) pearwood. Poor quality wood might only be used for the 'turned little boxes' (Table 7). These were probably a simple type of wooden horizontal compass dial, of which some examples have been recently found (fig. 132). Hardly any wooden diptychs survive, the most notable being two of 1511 and 1513 attributed to Erhard Etzlaub (fig. 55; Zinner I, 310), and one signed by Georg Reinmann (Zinner I, 484).

Significantly, there is no mention of brass among the materials laid down in the compass-makers' rules. This is despite the fact that all ivory diptych dials required at least some brass components, and that certain masters, notably Paul Reinmann and Thomas Tucher, used gilt brass extensively for decoration of their work. One example by Hans Tucher has an upper leaf of gilt brass and a lower leaf of ivory and wood (fig. 56). Examples of Nuremberg sundials made entirely in brass include those by Hans Gruber (fl. 1552), Hans Friessfeldt (1555), Paul Reinmann (1601), and Hans Troschel (1609) (Zinner I, 316, 327, 487, 552–3).

The reason for this omission of brass from the craft regulations is clear. Unlike their counterparts in Augsburg who were counted among the brass trades and produced clocks and other scientific instruments (Bobinger), the compass-makers of Nuremberg were firmly placed among the wood and turning trades. This enforced isolation from metal technology hindered diversification and may have contributed to the decline of their craft.

55 Diptych dial in boxwood, attributed to Erhard Etzlaub, Nuremberg, 1511.
GNM, WI 28. *(See also fig. 71)*.

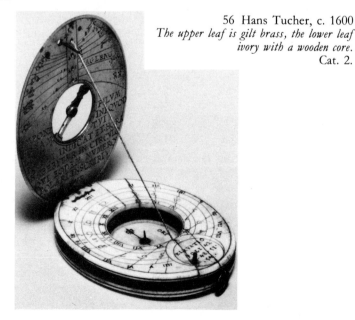

56 Hans Tucher, c. 1600
The upper leaf is gilt brass, the lower leaf ivory with a wooden core.
Cat. 2.

The masterpiece

The skills necessary to produce ivory and wooden diptychs were obviously transmitted orally, from master to apprentice. Because of a tradition of secrecy, very little is known today about the techniques used in manufacture, apart from that which can be gleaned from an examination of the instruments themselves. The regulations of the craft, however, do contain some details about the *masterpiece;* that is, the work that had to be produced and submitted by a journeyman before being admitted as a master. The basic requirements for this masterpiece remained essentially unchanged since 1535.

The would-be master had to produce punches or templates (*Stempfel*) of three different sizes; large, medium-sized and small. These would have been sets of punches that would have been necessary to stamp the letters, numbers and other motifs onto the ivory and brass. A dozen compasses had to be made for each size, presumably to ensure that the tools were durable enough for producing dials in considerable quantities. The rules also stated that the hour lines were to be in the centre of each dial and calibrated for a latitude of either 48°, or 49° 30′ for Nuremberg. (For a further discussion of latitudes on these instruments, see Chapter six).

The journeyman was expected to 'make and prepare the punches, compass and needle himself', but it is not clear whether he was supposed to make 'all the accessories' as well. Accessories used on each instrument included some or all of the following metal items: volvelles, wind vane, wind vane compartment cover, index arm, pin gnomons, hinges, clasps and fastenings, suspension ring and chain, ring to hold the compass glass, and decorative spandrels and feet. Most of these components in surviving instruments are made of brass, often gilded. Non-metal accessories include the glass of the compass bowl and the string for the gnomons. It cannot be established with any certainty which of these items were bought from other craftsmen and which were produced in the compass-maker's own workshop.

Makers' marks

The control of *marks* or signs was considered an important method of regulating quality. Like the coppersmiths and goldsmiths, each master compass-maker was meant to have only one sign. The design of his mark was not to be used or copied by anyone else and was seen as a measure preventing fraud. The penalty for infringement was two 'new' pounds, a sum which would not have been risked lightly by the ordinary craftsman (1 new pound = 4 old pounds = 120 pfennigs; Strauss, 203–4). A sample mark of each master, cut onto a die, was punched into a single piece of lead where all the signs were put together for easy comparison. The types of marks used fall into well-defined categories such as initials and numbers, animals and heraldic motifs (cf. fig. 105 below). They resemble those used by the Nuremberg coppersmiths and even trumpet-makers (Lockner; Wörthmüller).

The *sworn masters* responsible for enforcing the regulations, as in all the ordered crafts, had to check the work of the other masters at various stages of the manufacturing process. Each master himself had to stamp the compass when it was first designed and cut out from the wood or ivory. The instrument was inspected by a sworn master just before the needle and glass were inserted. If it were of sufficiently high quality the sworn master could stamp on an extra 'N' (for Nuremberg) as a sign of approval. Examples of such instruments can be seen in the exhibition, and their quality is obvious (fig. 57). Yet it must also be noted that the stamp does not seem to appear on instruments made after the first decade

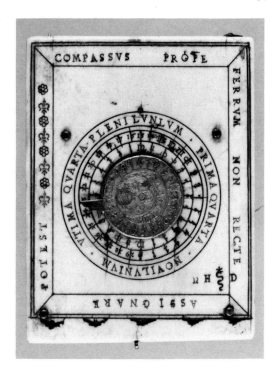

57 Hans Tucher, late 16th/early 17th century.
The 'N' punch is to the left of the maker's mark and initials 'HD'.
Cat. 50.

of the seventeenth century, which suggests that by that time it may have fallen into disuse.

Tools and materials

The buying of materials by craft members was also strictly regulated. All purchases of uncut ivory, wood, or tools made by an individual master were to be made known to the other members of the craft so that they could benefit from these transactions. For example, when a master bought needles from Weissenburg (a nearby town; see fig. 35) or elsewhere he was supposed to make half of the supply available to other members. If he made an exclusive deal with the supplier both were to be fined heavily – up to ten new pounds. He was also not supposed to sell materials or tools to others outside the craft. Such controls effectively prevented any attempts at undercutting prices or finding cheaper suppliers by individual masters for their personal gain. While these rules apparently operated for the collective benefit of the craft initially, in the longer term they probably had an inhibiting effect and eventually led to stagnation.

In the Nuremberg archives there are several inventories and wills made by compass-makers which refer to the tools of their craft. For example, according to the inventory drawn up by his widow Elisabeth in October 1529, Heinz Scheltner left tools for the making of compasses to the value of one guilder (NSA, *Inventarbücher des Stadtgerichts* Rep B 14, vol. 1, fol. 75ᵛ). The will of Sebalt Scheltner, dated January 1534, stipulates that his dwelling (on Paniersberg in St. Sebald's parish), his tools, 'with all accessories', and eighty guilders should be left to his son Michael, while four ivory teeth (tusks) and some cut bones should be shared between this son and a daughter, Margaretha Schneider (NSA, *Libri Litt.,* vol. 45, fol. 199/199ᵛ). The 1544 inventory of the compass-maker Fritz Pilgram and his wife Anna, who both died in 1543, includes the following items: two dials for compasses; about two pounds of cut ivory for compasses; and 'what else belongs to the making of compasses'. The total value of tools listed was six guilders (NSA, *Inventarbücher des Stadtgerichts* Rep B 14, vol. 3, fol. 54ᵛ).

58 Engraving of Georg Hartmann
(1489–1564) from a medallion of
1533
Johann Gabriel Doppelmayr, Historische
Nachricht Von den Nürnbergischen
Mathematicis und Künstlern
(Nuremberg, 1730), Table XIV.
Photograph by Ian Jones, London.

Craft disputes

Given there was such strict supervision of manufacture, it is hardly surprising to find that conflicts occurred between crafts whose work overlapped in some way. As can be seen from the regulations in Table 7, the compass-makers encroached on the craft of the mirror-makers or glaziers, while the vellum-makers in turn put their own compasses into writing tablets.

There were other threats to the craft. Already some time before 1565 an investigation was made into complaints by masters that cheap, shoddy instruments were being produced by some individuals from painted paper stuck onto wood. The penalty for producing instruments by such means was set at ten new pounds in order to discourage the practice. It is unlikely that the rule had any effect at all. The masters could not prevent anyone from making a cheap instrument from an existing print, which required no skill to produce. We might even assume that most instruments produced in the period were of such a type; that none of them survive shows that the fears of the masters were well-founded.

One person responsible for this development was undoubtedly Georg Hartmann (1489–1564; fig. 58). The evidence of Hartmann's career suggests that he was never a member of the compass-makers' craft. A pastor of St. Sebald's church in Nuremberg for many years, Hartmann was also a mathematician and designer of instruments such as astrolabes, quadrants and various types of sundials (Zinner I, 357–68). Between around 1527 and 1563 he published engravings of a whole range of instruments, including diptych dials and pillar dials. Such prints could easily be cut out and mounted onto wood or some other material (fig. 59). Alternatively, they might have been used as templates by compass-makers working in ivory. This is substantiated by a few surviving ivory diptychs with Hartmann's name on them (Plate II). Copies of many of Hartmann's paper designs are preserved in the Bayerische Staatsbibliothek, Munich. It may have

59 Engravings of the inner leaves of
three diptychs, calibrated for 50°
(1542), 44° (1535) and 50° 4′ (1538)
by Georg Hartmann.
The inscription of the first reads:
'Tempora labuntur tacitisque senescimus
annis/Et fugiunt freno non remorante dies'
*(the times slip away and we grow old with
the silently passing years; there is no
bridle that can curb the flying days: Ovid,
Fasti Bk 6, lines 771–2).*
BSB, MS Rar. 434, fol. 41.

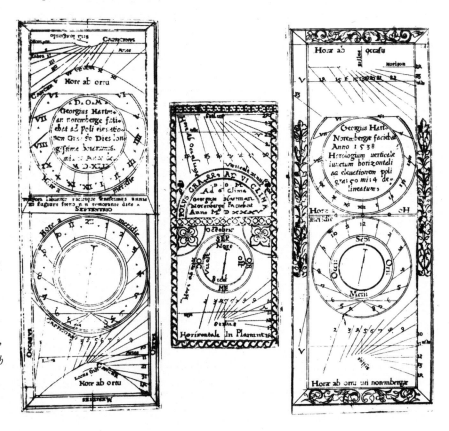

been in part due to Hartmann's activities that stricter controls over their production were introduced towards the end of the sixteenth century.

Evidence from the objects

The manufacture of ivory diptychs was relatively straight-forward. Although the various stages of production can be reconstructed, it is not possible to determine the division of labour between master, members of his workshop or outside contracted labour. In the compass-maker's workshop there would have been a furnace, tools and materials from outside suppliers, and specialist tools, which according to the regulations were fashioned by the master himself. Apparently even as late as 1548 the punches, which were a set part of the masterpiece, could be procured from specialist seal-engravers or iron-engravers (Hampe, nos 3108, 3119).

The illustrations of the two compass-makers at work from the Mendel *Hausbuch* provide some clues to the equipment they would have used. The anonymous compass-maker of 1549 is shown at his bench holding a file, with hammer, needles and glasses to hand. There is a small furnace in the background (fig. 45). Hans Tucher III is depicted holding a pair of dividers and a large ivory diptych dial. Spread out on the table in front of him are two other diptychs, some compass needles, a smaller pair of dividers, and a graver (Plate X). In each picture a sand-glass is shown, the familiar symbol of time-keeping as well as of transitoriness.

An insight into the manufacturing process can be gained from an examination of the instruments themselves, supplemented by information from a range of printed sources.

Preparing the ivory

A tusk was first selected and sawn into different-sized slabs using a thin-bladed steel saw to minimize wastage. Some care was necessary to use the material economically. Large tablets would be taken from the centre of the tusk, smaller pieces from the outer edges, being cut longitudinally along the grain (fig. 24; Holtzapffel, vol. 1, 146). Once a slab for a dial plate was cut to the correct size and thickness (usually between 5–8 mm), the first stage of flattening and smoothing it could take place. The slab was probably rubbed on a hard flat sandstone block and then smoothed on a finer stone block dipped in water.

Small holes, such as those for the hinges, were made with an ordinary bow drill, while larger holes, such as the compass viewing-hole, might have required the use of a brace and bit, or even a lathe (fig. 60). The compass bowl and scaphe hollows were certainly produced by fixing the dial plate onto a small lathe, turned by hand or perhaps with a treadle, and cutting it with hand-held steel tools (Moxon, 212–3; Holtzapffel, vol. 2, 517–9; Woodbury, 38–71). Straight lines (borders, hour lines, etc.) would either be laid out and drawn by hand using a ruler and graver, or else marked more quickly with the aid of a wooden dividing template. The dial could be placed in the centre of the template which would have pegs for the ruler to rest against. Circles were generated by a hand-held dividing compass with a steel pointer or a rigid beam compass, but some makers probably relied on templates for marking these as well (*History of Technology,* vol. 3, 620–31).

Ivory was engraved using the same techniques as those required for brass or wood (fig. 61; Bosse; Hind). A design, copied from an existing drawing or pattern, would be traced lightly on the surface and then incised

60 The Woodturner
Hans Sachs and Jost Ammann,
Eygentliche Beschreibung aller
Stände auff Erden *(Frankfurt, 1568).*

using a sharp-pointed steel graver (or burin).   Letters, numbers, zodiac signs, small decorative motifs and the maker's mark were all added by punching stamps onto the surface.

According to Michel, the surface would previously have been softened with a special preparation in order to prevent the ivory from cracking when hit with the punches.   Both he and Maskell refer to the existence of several ancient recipes for softening ivory.   Yet as Burack has pointed out, such recipes were apparently intended to make a curved piece of ivory malleable enough to flatten, not to soften it for punching.   Apparently all modern attempts to recreate these recipes have met with failure.   Without further investigation it would seem that the theory mentioned by Michel remains unproven (Michel I, 161; Maskell, 176; Burack, 43–5).

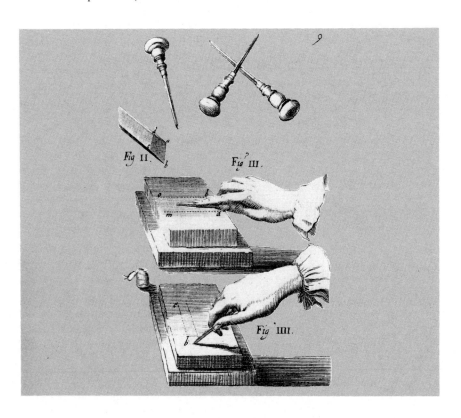

61 Use of the burin
Abraham Bosse, Traicté des Manières de Graver en Taille-Douce *ed. Le Clerc (Paris, 1701), Plate IX.*
Oxford, Bodleian Library, Douce B. 678.

The production and use of the punches, derived from contemporary goldsmithing, coining and print techniques, comprised the most skilled part of the entire manufacturing process (Theophilus, 91–2; Moxon, 59–62; Holtzapffel, vol. 2, 926; *History of Technology,* vol. 3, 383–90). A length of steel rod could be bought ready-made and sawn into smaller lengths from which the punches could be prepared. The tip of each punch would be carefully hand sawn, chiselled and filed while the steel was in a fully annealed (soft) state. To harden the finished punch, it would be placed in a furnace until cherry-red in colour, rapidly cooled by quenching with water or oil, and then re-heated to a much lower temperature to prevent it from becoming too brittle. Examples of imperfect marks on various dials show how small bits would sometimes break off from the top of the punch.

A punch was impressed into the ivory with a blow from a hammer. This process had the effect of forcing the material upwards; any burr had to be smoothed down by filing or rubbing on sandstone. A final polish could be given by the use of a powder of fine sandstone or chalk mixed with water and applied with a cloth to the surface of the ivory which would then be rubbed over with a dry woollen cloth.

Pigments and dyes

The pigments used to colour the engraving and punch marks were prepared using a variety of techniques similar to those used for paints. It is likely that the compass-makers would have been able to buy most of the pigments they used ready prepared, since in Nuremberg there was enough demand from craftsmen for their production to be commercially viable.

There are five principal colours found on the diptych dials: black, red, green, blue and orange/brown (see Plates). The composition of the inorganic pigments (red, green and blue) was identified using X-ray fluorescence analysis (XRF), a method of non-destructive surface analysis in which X-rays are used to produce a spectrum in which the peaks represent the different elements. For the organic pigments (black, orange/brown) other techniques were used such as scanning electron microscopy (SEM), where electrons create images of samples under high magnification with an associated X-ray analytical facility (Henderson, Mortimer & Hackmann; cf. Winter). This scientific information can be supplemented with historical details from documentary sources about techniques of manufacturing pigments (Theophilus; Agricola; Harley; Gettens & Stout).

There were traditionally three principal sources of black pigment: soot from burnt wood, lamp black (collected from a smoky oil or wax flame on a cold surface) or ivory black. This was produced by the incineration of ivory chips in a closed vessel heated over a charcoal fire (Harley, 148–9). Analysis of the particles of black used on some of the dials, which were elemental carbon, suggests that the latter technique was favoured. This particular method would have provided an economical use of any spare ivory chips. As an exhaustive analysis of the pigment from all the dials has not been made, however, the use of the other forms of black cannot be excluded. In any case, the black powder, like the other pigments, appears to have been mixed with a binding material of egg white, glue or beeswax before being applied to the surface (Gettens & Stout, 5, 19–20). Several dials examined were found to have the various pigments in a wax binder on the outer leaf and a water soluble binder inside; of course, the wax might also have been applied accidentally through polishing practices.

Analysis of the red pigment showed that it was basically vermilion, a powder made from cinnabar, or red mercuric sulphide, incorporated in ground glass. In addition to the main components of mercury and sulphur it contained lead, phosphorus and soda, magnesia, alumina and silica, although the percentages of these were not determined. Red mercuric sulphide occurs as a natural ore in volcanic sites such as Etna or Vesuvius, but it was already being manufactured in Europe for use as a pigment from the early medieval period. By the sixteenth century cinnabar was relatively inexpensive and the best bright red available. The process of making the pigment was straightforward but tedious, and chemical apparatus was required for the sublimation of the mercury and sulphur mix (Theophilus, 40; Harley, 114–7). All this suggests that the compass-maker bought his red pigment already prepared – perhaps from a glass manufacturer – and simply had to mix it with a binding material before application.

The green pigment was found to be principally composed of copper in association with a trace of zinc and iron, incorporated in ground glass containing magnesia, soda, alumina, silica, phosphorous and calcium oxide. In other words, it was verdigris or copper acetate mixed with ground glass. Verdigris (which means green of the Greeks) was a colour used since antiquity, being relatively easy to prepare. Instructions for producing it can be found in manuscripts of the sixteenth century and earlier. The most common method was to expose copper to the fumes given off from fermenting grape skins or placing copper over vinegar or sour red wine in a sealed vessel. The green deposit which gradually accumulated could be scraped off the copper and made into a powder which had to be mixed with beeswax or other binding material before being applied. By the seventeenth century, verdigris was being produced commercially in large quantities; one of the main centres for its production was Montpellier (Harley, 73–5). The Nuremberg compass-maker probably acquired his green from a more local source.

The blue pigment was found to contain cobalt as the major colourant, associated with copper, arsenic, iron and nickel in a potassium lime silica glass. This solution of cobalt oxide in glass is known as 'smalt', a word which was already used as early as 1492. Cobalt minerals were first discovered in mines on the borders of Saxony and Bohemia in the early fifteenth century. Although the technique for producing smalt was of either Italian or German invention, the credit is usually given to a Bohemian glass-maker, Christian Schürner. He initially used his method at Neudeck around 1540 before transmitting it first to Nuremberg and then Holland, where high quality smalt was produced commercially in the seventeenth century. Cobalt ore was heated to form an oxide and mixed with silica and potash. While only about 3 per cent was required for the blue in normal 'stained glass', about 10–20 per cent of cobalt oxide had to be added to make the glass blue enough for powdering (Harley, 513; Gettens & Stout, 157–8).

The orange/brown pigment was provisionally identified as being a dye made from a red wood, possibly brasil. This is a hard brown-red wood from the tree genus *Caesalpinia,* found in the East Indies and South America. Once the trade routes with these countries were operating, brasil wood was imported in blocks which were then rasped and reduced to a coarse powder. In England during the seventeenth century this powder was only about 10*d* a pound, and was much cheaper than cochineal. The powder was prepared by soaking and boiling in a mixture of water and vinegar. Alum was added, and the colour tempered with a solution of gum. A more concentrated form could be obtained by boiling the dye in a pan (Harley, 132–4).

Needles, glass and string

As already mentioned, the master was supposed to make his needles himself, but as the regulations indicate, they could also be bought in from elsewhere. Each stage of manufacture, from the first production of steel to the final shaping of the needles, was a process undertaken by specialized metalworkers. To make steel, iron ore and charcoal (carbon) were heated up in a furnance; the red-hot ore was then hammered out and folded over many times (like making puff pastry!) to produce a hard sheet of steel (Agricola, 423–6). This sheet could be cut into the required shapes. The needles were either magnetized by a lodestone, or else the steel sheet had already been magnetized in the production process by quenching it from red heat in line with the earth's magnetic field. Such a method is illustrated in William Gilbert's *De magnete* of 1600. Given that the making of compass needles was part of the masterpiece, and the fact that the needles are still magnetic today, it is reasonable to assume that the latter process was employed.

The glass covers of fifteen diptych dials in the Oxford collection were analysed with electron probe microanalysis (EPMA), a technique using an electron beam to analyse chemically selected small areas of sample (Henderson, Mortimer & Hackmann). All the pieces analysed were basically of potassium oxide silica glass, with a single exception which was of a soda lime silica glass (Cat. 52). Of the remaining examples, only three appeared to be genuinely old glass (Cats. 39, 42, 45), since they contained significantly more magnesia and calcium oxide than the rest, which are probably modern replacement covers.

62 1611, with crown mark, probably Reinmann workshop
*The glass in the compass bowl appears to be genuinely old. The vignette on the lower leaf portrays the Woman of the Apocalypse, standing on the crescent moon (*Revelation *12.1).*
Cat. 45.

The compass-maker regulations refer to a dispute with the glaziers over glass used in the dials (Table 7).   It seems likely that the glass, which is of fairly low quality, was not made by the compass masters but bought in as ready-made discs.   The edges of each disc had to be bevelled in order to provide a tight fit for fastening it with a wire or string in the compass bowl.

That the strings used for the gnomons were also of inferior quality is suggested by an analysis made on a selection of diptychs in the Oxford collection (Crawforth).   They appear to have been made from hand-spun silk fibres using the simplest of tools such as hand-held hooks.   Two strands of thread were lightly twisted together, producing a cord of irregular diameter and hairy appearance.   Most of the strings assumed to be original are either a natural beige colour (Cats. 26, 34) or stained with various shades of green (Cats. 10, 17, 55).   There is one example of red string, which matches the colouring in the engraving (Cat. 15).   The primitive construction of these strings contrasts strikingly with the high quality of these found on small German and French balances from the same period.

The strings were found to be attached to the body of the dial in one of two ways.   The common method was to pass the string through a hole drilled in the body and tying a knot, which was then concealed in a countersunk depression in the outer part of the hole.   Another method used a small wooden plug to wedge the string in the hole.   In a few cases, the end of the knotted cord is covered by a brass volvelle.   Only in these examples, and where there is no sign that the volvelle has been removed, can it be assumed that the cord is not a replacement (Cat. 3).

Brass fittings

Using XRF, the original brass fittings were shown to contain between 18 and 22 per cent zinc (standard for this period), with small amounts of lead and tin.   Nickel was also often detected, up to about 0.5 per cent, and arsenic, silver and antimony were occasionally found in even smaller quantities (Henderson, Mortimer & Hackmann).   It appears that this brass was made by the calamine technique.   Here calamine (zinc carbonate) was added to molten copper in a crucible.   Carbon and oxygen was given off as carbon dioxide while the other impurities formed, with silica, a slag that could be skimmed off the surface of the smolten metal.   Both antimony and arsenic in small quantities harden the finished metal.   Lead, on the other hand, has the effect of increasing the fluidity of the molten metal and thus helps considerably in the production of high-quality casting, a process which was obviously used for some of the finer accessories on the dials (Agricola, Book 9, especially 400–5; Hodges, 69).

In Nuremberg, a major centre for brass manufacture, brass could easily be bought in the form of sheets or wire to be cut and shaped to requirements.   Hinges, clasps and compass rings were usually made from wire.   The gnomon pins were hammered directly into the ivory and consisted of brass or bronze.

The brass volvelles found on the ivory diptychs were obviously made by two different methods.   The first used the techniques already described for marking the ivory: a blank disc was graved and punched with steel tools, possibly using a template (Plate XII).   The second method used coining techniques (*History of Technology*, vol. 2, 185–6).   Here a blank pellet of brass was heated up on an anvil and then hit with a round die stamp on which the numbers and lines had already been cut out in relief.   The entire surface of the volvelle was struck at a single blow (fig. 63).

63 Hans Troschel, late 16th/early
17th century
*Leaf 2b, showing a lunar volvelle with a
stamped brass disc. The maker's mark of
a thrush on a twig is punched thrice at the
base of the leaf.*
Cat. 13.

The brass decoration on the diptychs was in most cases presumably
gilded, although the gilt has worn away on many examples. For the
analysis of the brass, non-gilded samples were selected, since gilt obscures
the other information from the XRF technique. Consequently there are
no results for the analysis of gilt. The process of gilding is fairly well
documented, however (e.g. Theophilus, 113–4, 145–6; Agricola, 460,
464).

Fine gold was warmed with mercury for some time at a temperature of
about 80°C, producing a paste known as gold amalgam. Meanwhile, the
brass would be dipped in acid and rubbed over with a solution of mercury
nitrate, leaving a thin film of mercury. Gold amalgam was spread on a
smooth stone and a brass wire brush rubbed over it to pick up the
paste. The brush was then rubbed over the prepared surface of the brass,
covering it in gold amalgam. Once the coated brass was placed in a steel
ladle and heated in a charcoal furnace, the mercury boiled off, leaving a
thin layer of gold covering the brass. When the metal had cooled, the gilt
could be polished using another clean brass wire brush.

The process of gilding could have taken place in a compass-maker's
workshop. Since this was a highly specialized process, it is more likely
that completed brass fittings were sent to a goldsmith who accepted such
commissions. In 1534, for example, Georg Hartmann was granted permission to have a brass compass-dial gilded (Hampe, no. 2063).

The investigation of the manufacturing process of the dials reveals the
extent to which the compass-maker could rely on the skills and techniques
of other craftsmen in the city. Along with the basic materials of ivory
and brass, specialist tools, pigments and accessories were all immediately
available for purchase in Nuremberg. Workmen from all kinds of trades
could be readily employed to undertake simple, repetitive tasks. It is
apparent that the design of the diptych dial lent itself to serial production
of certain basic components in relatively large quantities. Only the final
layout of the design and ornament distinguished one dial from
another. As will be shown in the following chapter, the technical and
ornamental resources used in their design relied either directly or indirectly on the skills of the professional mathematician/astronomer, and the
printer/engraver. Engraving was the mediating principle which effected
the link between designer and craftsman (fig. 64).

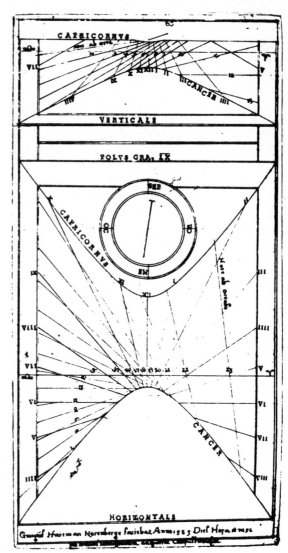

64 Engraving of inner leaves of
diptych for latitude 60°, 1535, Georg
Hartmann
The inscription beneath reads 'pro utilitate
horologistarum vulgariter compastmacher.'
(For the use of the 'horologistae'
commonly known as compass-makers).
BSB, MS Rar. 434, fol. 58.

TABLE 7: Compass-Makers' Statute of 1608

Duty of the sworn [*masters* added in most manuscripts]	The two [*three* in earlier and later versions of the statute] masters of the compass-makers who are ordained and installed as Sworn [*Geschworene*; adjudicators of the craft, vetted by the City Council] at times, should promise and swear that they will faithfully preside over and maintain the craft, that they will promote the profit and benefit of said craft and of the city in general; and that they undertake to work diligently so that the same [sc., the craft's] and the following [sc., the city's] statutes are kept. And wherever they should learn and perceive that the laid down laws and statutes are being contravened, that they would report this to the clerk of the *Rugamt* [obviously a kind of Industrial Council; in the 1535 version the officer to be contacted was the Bailiff] and, as is the usage in other crafts, they will reprimand [the offender], faithfully and without any danger [to themselves].
Joint voting	On no account should they be present, nor attend nor partake of, neither should they wish to do so, if in their craft any penalty, fine, prohibition or joint voting is being taken in hand in any matter without the permission of An Honourable Council [this is the style of the City Council throughout these documents]. On the contrary, wherever they hear of such or notice something similar, which might be, or would have been taken in hand and enacted in opposition to An Honourable Council, they undertake, on their oath, to report and to make this known at the same hour to a *Burgermeister*.

[These clauses appear here for the first time as a preamble, in 1535 they formed paragraphs one and two of the statute; the latter injunction obviously aims at preventing any attempt at self-legislation.]

Thereupon follow the articles.

An apprentice is to learn for four years and must be registered with the clerk of the *Rugamt*	First. If henceforward a master of this said craft wishes to take on and accept an apprentice, he should take him on initially for fourteen days' probation, and if thereupon he is satisfied with him, he shall contract and take him on for no less than four years in order to teach him. And he must also have him registered with the clerk of the *Rugamt,* subject to a fine of five new pounds.

[The original three years of apprenticeship were extended to four years only on 16 January 1579; the fine was increased from one new pound.]

Apprentices to be contracted in the presence of the sworn master	Second. From now on no master shall accept nor hire an apprentice without the knowledge and presence of the sworn masters, so that the apprentice will be registered more likely and more certainly with the clerk of the *Rugamt*, subject to a fine of two pounds new *Heller*.

[Whereas the pound was a convenient unit for reckoning only, the *Heller* was a coin actually in circulation in Nuremberg; one new pound was the equivalent of 240 *Heller*.]

Number of apprentices and journeymen	Third. No master should have more than one apprentice and one journeyman, subject to the below-mentioned fine.
All apprentices to be made *Burger* within eight weeks	Fourth. It shall be the duty of each master of the compass-maker's craft (just like other masters of closed crafts here) not to take on a foreigner as apprentice, or someone who is not the child of a *Burger*, without previously having obtained the permission of a Noble, Honourable Council. In the case of permission being granted by their Lords to take on such a person who is not a *Burger* nor the child of a *Burger*, he should, as soon as he is required to do so, bring him before the *Burger-Herren* and have him made a *Burger,* subject to a fine of ten new pounds.

[In the later 1570s there was apparently some discussion whether such citizenship had to be acquired at the beginning or the end of one's apprenticeship; on 5 September 1578, it was decreed that in the closed crafts this should happen within a fortnight from the contracting of an apprentice; that period was apparently at some point extended to eight weeks.]

Pause

Fifth.   When a master has completed the four years' teaching of an apprentice he has to pause for a year and does not have the right to take on another apprentice before its end, subject to a fine of two new pounds.

Work two years as a journeyman

Sixth.   A person who has completed the four years' training is to work a further two years afterwards in the craft as a journeyman, before being admitted to the master's title.

[This seems rather to refer to the master's examination. The original period of one year's work as a journeyman was extended to two years on 11 September 1565; this injunction was confirmed on 16 January 1579, together with the extension of apprenticeship to four years.]

Concerning the masterpiece

Seventh.   Whoever wishes to become a compass-maker master and work in the same craft must first make the following masterpieces, namely three punches [*Stempfel*, which may mean the tool for punching as well as the image created by punching], a large one, a medium-sized one, which is called *Genffer* [i.e., from Geneva] since old times, and a small one.   [They are to be made] in a way that all the hours are shown in the centre and its circle [surround], from which all hours flow.   The usual height should be of approximately eight and nine-a-half and forty degrees, as the pole is here at Nuremberg.   In addition, for every punch there should be a dozen compasses including the needle with all accessories.   [All that in order to prove] that the same [aspiring master] can make and produce everything such as punches, compasses and needles himself, and if he does not pass with his masterpieces, he must pause for a quarter of a year and work as a journeyman, and during such time he cannot be admitted to the master's title [or master's examination].

[This paragraph is consistent in its wording with the regulations for masterpieces in earlier versions of the statute, except for the formula for the pole-height: *eight* or *nine a-half and forty degrees.*]

Masterpieces to be made in the workshop of a Sworn [master]

Eighth.   Each person who wishes to become a master in this craft shall also be duty bound and obliged to make his pieces at a sworn master's [under his supervision], and to draw his own design.

[This stipulation concerning supervision and original design was decreed on 18 July 1562, initiated by a supplication of the compass-makers themselves.]

Compasses to be made of good boxwood or ivory

Ninth.   Each compass-maker should henceforward only work, in-lay or make each and every compass from no other timber than good boxwood, pearwood or ivory, except for turned little boxes, for which the covers and top lids only may be of inferior wood.   All subject to a fine of four new guilders.

[The pearwood represents a relaxation of the original restrictions. The fine is referred to as four new pounds in other manuscripts.]

Concerning the marks

Tenth.   Each master should have his own mark, and such marks should be struck all together in lead, so that one might see and perceive that no master is copying or almost copying another's mark; as is already customary here in more other crafts.   And each person is to use only one mark, all subject to a fine of two new pounds.

No one to punch another's mark

Eleventh.   No pieceworker shall henceforward punch his principal's mark onto his own work, but each such pieceworker must use his own mark on his own work, subject to the fine mentioned below.

[This stipulation is a shortened version of injunctions enacted on 8 February 1564]

Each person is to sign his own work, to have the sworn masters judge it and have it stamped with the N

Twelfth.   Each master should mark and sign his piece of wood with his own mark when it is designed or engraved but before it is cut off and brought for inspection.   Then when the compasses have reached the stage of having the mirror-quality glass and the needle inserted in their place, and [the compass is] marked in this manner, they must be brought for inspection before the sworn masters for the time being, to whom An Honourable Council has granted that they punch an N as an additional mark, which they always have at hand, and therein they act according to their duty to nobody's advantage nor harm, honourably and without suspicion.   Therefore they have free and open access to inspect the work in the master's workshop at any time, and if they find bad, poorly-made work or something wrong, they seize this; yet they do not change [such work] nor punish, but on each occasion they bring what can be corrected before the *Rugherren,* and await a decision from there.   The fine for the offenders, who have violated the rules shall be set at five new pounds.

[These descriptions of the duties and rights of the sworn masters, especially concerning the additional N-mark appear for the first time in a decree of the Council dated 11 September 1565. The comprehensive inspection rights had already been granted on 18 July 1562.]

Concerning the paper adornment of compasses

Thirteenth.   Compasses should be drawn and divided freehand, but until now compasses have been covered with painted paper which does not endure and is a mere deception through which the buyer is cheated.   Such work gains ground and gives the craft a bad reputation, and therefore shall from now on such deceit and badly done work be completely stopped, and attract a fine of ten new pounds.   And every master shall draw, divide and decorate the compasses freehand, according to the masterpiece and in the manner of the craft, on good boxwood without any paper fraud.   Yet as regards the box where the wood can clearly be recognized, it should remain unmarked furthermore.   However, it is the duty of each compass-maker to leave the marks plain and uncoloured, and to punch it so that it may be clearly seen, and the master be recognised, subject to the above fine.

[Such clarification was issued by the Council on 22 April 1574, in order to end a dispute within the craft of compass-makers. It seems that the sworn masters had wished that from now on the maker's mark should be punched into the compass-bowl but Council found it more important that the working material might be recognized therein.]

Publicize all working materials

Fourteenth.   In future, a master of the said craft shall not buy any cut or uncut boxwood, ivory or other working material for himself alone.   Rather, it is his duty to make such buys known, so that every master can come into the same cheap buy.   And any master who buys such materials and does not let it be known in the craft shall be punished for every undisclosed load and give ten new pounds.

Needles not to be sold outside the craft

Fifteenth.   No resident compass-maker should from now on have power to sell to a trader or other person, here or elsewhere, needles belonging to the compass, whether or not they have been declared.   They must remain in the craft and are not to be sold or sent to anyone else, either from here or to a stranger, who is not in the craft, subject to a fine of five guilders.

[On 21 November 1542, the sale of needles was only prohibited if not beforehand disclosed to all the members of the craft; the fine was set to ten new pounds, in line with the previous paragraph. The new restrictions came into force on 19 March 1575. The fine would seem to be slightly more than ten new pounds.]

A master who buys needles from outside shall keep no more than half the portion

Sixteenth. Whenever a master from here buys or orders needles from Weissenburg or from other places, he should not keep more than half of these materials for himself. It is his duty then to make known the other half to the craft. Also he who buys needles, which have not been made public beforehand by the seller, will be reprimanded as well as the seller, and for both the fine will be set at ten new pounds.

Concerning commissions outside the city

Seventeenth. As regards commissioning of work outside of the city, that should be conducted in accordance with the spirit and letter of the law about it, which is common to all craftsmen.

Concerning the insertion of compasses in writing tablets

Eighteenth. The parchment makers and others, who do not belong to the compass-makers' craft, shall be stopped and they shall be forbidden to encroach further onto the compass-makers by inserting compasses into writing tablets and other things, subject to a fine of five new pounds.

[This injunction was originally granted against a named parchment maker, Gregor Spengler, but now translated into a general rule. Such writing tablets must have been similar to the gilt copper instrument made in Prague by Erasmus Habermehl in the late sixteenth century which is part of the Billmeir Collection (Inv. no. 57–84/198), now at the Museum of the History of Science, Oxford.]

Concerning the insertion of the mirror-quality glass

Nineteenth. As concerns the insertion of the mirror-quality glass in the compasses, about which from misconceptions between the glaziers and compass-makers all sorts of disagreement arose, the following clarification was made by An Honourable Council. That the compass-makers from now on, in spite of the glaziers, may insert the mirror-quality glass in the three types of the Genffer compasses from the smallest to the biggest; but the compass-makers are no longer to insert a glass in the round and square little boxes, buttons, containers, whatever they may be called, subject to a fine of ten new pounds.

[On 21 November 1542, this dispute was decided in favour of the compass-makers. The ruling had a wording very similar to this paragraph, and the fine was set at two new pounds. The glaziers got their way on 10 October 1556, and a fine was set at ten new pounds. It would seem that such restriction proved impractical and was renounced in due course.]

No peddling of work

Twentieth. No master shall peddle his work in the pubs or on the streets here, subject to a fine of five new pounds.

[This prohibition was added on 16 January 1579, initially with reference to journeymen who peddled their masterpieces.]

All maids and daughters who marry outside of the guild not to be commissioned [with work]

Twenty-first. Henceforward all maids as well as the masters' daughters who marry others outside of their craft shall, subject to a fine of five new pounds, by no means be commissioned with work of the compass-makers.

[This amendment to the statute was decreed on 10 March 1590.]

Master's sons with journeymen to attend at the lodge

Twenty-second. It is the duty of the masters' sons, as soon as they are sixteen and up until their eighteenth year, with and besides the journeymen to attend [meetings of] their lodge every two months and to maintain their craft's customs.

[The inclusion of this and the following paragraphs into the statute cannot be dated with certainty. Presumably, they are taken from legislation for all the closed crafts, and here applied explicitly to the compass-makers for the first time.]

Masters' sons and journeymen not to leave the city without the knowledge of the sworn [masters]

Twenty-third. While the compass-makers' craft in this town is a closed one and the journeymen and sons of the masters are not allowed to travel [as itinerant workers in their own craft], it happens that sometimes someone does leave under the pretext that he has some other business to attend to, and remains outside the

PLATE X: Hans Tucher III
Hausbuch der Mendelschen Zwölfbrüderstiftung II, fol. 108ᵛ
Nuremberg, Stadtbibliothek. Photograph by Foto Hilbinger GmbH, Schwaig-Behringersdorf.

PLATE XI: Divider-smith
Hausbuch der Mendelschen Zwölfbrüderstiftung II, fol. 107ᵛ
Nuremberg, Stadtbibliothek. Photograph by Foto Hilbinger GmbH, Schwaig-Behringersdorf.

city for some time. Since one cannot know, if in the meantime he has worked at other places, from now on every journeyman or master's son, who wants to leave here on account of other business, shall announce this beforehand to the sworn masters, and in case that they suspect, that someone might work in his handicraft outside, then they shall report that [suspicion] to the *Rugherren,* and await further decision.

Masters and journeymen to meet every eight weeks from now on

Twenty-fourth. The masters and journeymen shall from now on no longer meet, as has been happening in the past, at their lodge every four weeks but every eight weeks, and there it is a master's duty to pay five *Creuzer* [subscription] and a journeyman three *Creuzer.* This and the previous two articles are subject to a fine of five new pounds.

[One *Creuzer,* a coin in circulation here although not minted in Nuremberg, represented the sixtieth part of a new pound.]

No marriage before completion of the masterpieces

Twenty-fifth. Any journeyman of this craft who marries before completion of his masterpieces and attaining the title of a master, shall no longer be admitted to the mentioned masterpieces.

[In one manuscript of 1629, this paragraph is added in another hand and ascribed to a decree of 25 September 1669, but in other manuscripts of 1608 and 1629 it appears to be in the original hand. It is most likely that the stipulation, as the previous three paragraphs, stems from legislation common to all closed crafts in Nuremberg.]

Compass-makers .14.

From the 1719 description of all crafts by the *Rugamt* in a manuscript commemorating the splendour of Nuremberg handicrafts in the past (see also Plate XVIII)

The craft of the compass-makers is of great reputation, because they made several types of compasses from wood, ivory and brass, in various forms, such as in the form of little books, violins, lutes, rings and many other types. These have been occasionally exported, even to distant-lying provinces and kingdoms. They also have made quadrants in various ways for all types of hours, such as the German, the Bohemian, as well as ship and night compasses. But now there are fewer masters than before, and there also is less work, so that they can do very little about it [the decline of their craft]. It is a closed craft, in that they are not allowed to travel outside in order to work in the same, otherwise they would be acting dishonestly and breaking their oath. The masterpieces for a sworn-in master consist of 3 dozen boxwood compasses of various sizes, also of 3 punches, whereby the path to the hour number is drawn onto the compasses, and then they have to design a quadrant freehand.

[The '14' in the title might refer to the number of masters in the craft at the time of writing.]

CHAPTER SIX

What was the technical and decorative context?

By the time the oldest dated instrument in this exhibition was produced (fig. 46), the compass-making trade was already an established manufacturing craft in Nuremberg.   In fact, most surviving diptychs date from a relatively late phase in the craft's development.   Although the ornamentation on the diptychs underwent certain stylistic changes, their technical specifications remained almost unmodified during this period.

The functional and decorative aspects of the Nuremberg ivory diptychs complemented each other, as is found in other instruments of the period (Rohde, 5–9; Michel II, 10–11).   The overall layout of each diptych, including the arrangement of the dial furniture and the ornamental engraving and punching, resulted in an attractive appearance which ensured that it was a precious and pleasing artefact as well as a useful device.   The compass-makers were general artisans who presumably had no training in theoretical gnomonics.   Yet their instruments incorporated technical features which suggests that they were copied from designs that were initially provided by the collaboration between a mathematician and engraver.   These could be either in the form of drawings or prints.

A similar observation can be made about the sources of the ornamental engraving found on the sundials.   Whoever actually incised the patterns on each instrument would have been following a design, either by copying freehand or else by means of a paper template.   A study of the ornament reveals the existence of a variety of standardized motifs and patterns common to more than one maker, although individual characteristics can also be identified.   A comparison of the diptychs with other decorated artefacts such as guns, watches and silverware made in Nuremberg and elsewhere during the period reveals that a similar ornamental vocabulary was employed in all of these crafts.   The readiest source for the compass-makers' inspiration was the large number of pattern books published in Nuremberg by goldsmiths and engravers (fig. 65) from the mid-sixteenth century onwards.

65 Frontispiece of a pattern book by Georg Bang, c. 1620
GNM, K 3550.

Engraving and prints in Nuremberg

Nuremberg was the most active print centre in Germany in the sixteenth century.   For engraving and graphic design it was matched only by Paris, Antwerp and Augsburg (Irmscher, 141).   The type of prints produced in Nuremberg included both artistic and scientific material, ranging from maps, globes and mathematical texts to emblem books, portraits and landscapes (e.g. fig. 36).   Apart from their many other artistic and social functions, prints also indirectly transformed the method of producing artefacts.   They were a commodity that was easily transferred between the shop of the engraver and that of the craftsman who copied them (Melot, 23–57).

The activities of goldsmiths appear to have been responsible for the earliest development of engraving and print technology.   The technique

66 Beaker ornamented with
strapwork of leaves, flowers and fruit
by Bernhard Zan, 1580
Dotted-print or stipple engraving
(Punzenstich).
GNM, K 12772.

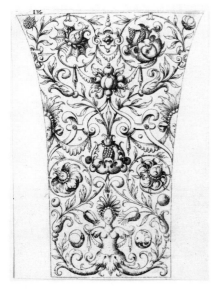

67 Ornamental beaker designed by
Johann Sibmacher and engraved by
Hieronymus Bang, 1596
GNM, K 11782.

of making prints from metal plates into which a design has been incised
evolved independently in both the Rhine valley and Italy in the mid-
fifteenth century, and soon became commercialized. The individual primarily responsible for the public acceptance of the engraved print as a
significant artistic product was Albrecht Dürer, who was himself the son
of a Nuremberg goldsmith.

Apprentice goldsmiths in Nuremberg were trained in the art of die
cutting as well as the skills of casting and jewellery making, a technique
which was of use in a variety of crafts. It was an integral part of
typefounding, for example, and also the production of punches used on
diptychs. Journeymen goldsmiths were allowed to supplement their
income by producing engraved pattern books specifically for the use of
master goldsmiths or other craftsmen (Hayward, 38–42). These
appeared in great numbers from the mid-decades of the sixteenth century,
and were subsequently copied and reprinted both in Nuremberg and
elsewhere. The influence of such patterns on the decoration of diptych
dials is first apparent from the very end of the sixteenth century, notably
in the instruments of Paul Reinmann (Plate IV).

Of the many individuals who produced pattern books in sixteenth- and
seventeenth-century Nuremberg, a few deserve particular mention. The
leading master of German ornament in the middle of the sixteenth century
was the Nuremberg painter and graphic designer Virgil Solis
(1514–1562). He published innumerable collections of designs copied
from those of different engravers under his own name or initials
(O'Dell-Franke; Berliner, 62–3). Many of these designs were in the form
of strips or borders to be adapted for different objects, materials and
spaces. Their ornamentation included scrollwork, strapwork, arabesques and grotesques with a variety of exotic flora and fauna. One type
of border made popular by Solis, who borrowed it from the earlier
so-called 'small masters' or *Kleinmeister* was the hunting scene in linear
form with huntsmen, running dogs, stags, hares and other animals. Solis's designs were widely copied and imitated throughout
Europe over the next hundred years.

Bernhard Zan (fl. 1580–81) and Paul Flindt the younger (1567-after
1631) were two later goldsmith-engravers who produced designs of
objects intended principally for goldsmiths. In their patterns for cups,
candlesticks, goblets, and the like, they employed a new dotted-print
technique (*Punzenstiche* – stipple engraving) which was taken directly from
the goldsmith's craft. Lines were not incised with a burin on the plate,
but instead consisted of a series of tiny dots made by a punch (fig. 66;
Berliner, 80; Hayward, 237; Irmscher). Another contemporary painter-
engraver, Johann Sibmacher (fl. 1590–d. 1611), employed the established
engraving techniques for similar designs (fig. 67; Berliner, 77). As will
be shown, some motifs, particularly those of urns and flowers, found on
the diptychs are strongly reminiscent of those used by Zan, Flindt and
Sibmacher.

The group of Nuremberg goldsmith-engravers whose work seems to
overlap most obviously with that of the compass-makers were members
of one family. The eldest of these, Hieronymus Bang (1553–1630), was
born in Osnabrück and arrived in Nuremberg in 1587. He became a
master goldsmith a year later. Theodor and Georg Bang (d. 1654)
became masters in 1606 and 1626 respectively (Berliner, 66, 78, 81;
Irmscher). It was around the same period when decorative motifs began
to be employed extensively on the ivory diptychs. Examples of birds,
flowers and fruits in designs by the Bangs resemble similar motifs on the
instruments. The matching of patterns with instruments must remain
impressionistic, however, since no exact copies have yet been found.

Astronomy and geography in Nuremberg

The astronomical and geographical information required for the use of diptychs was similar to that involved in the production of calendars, almanacs, ephemerides, maps, charts and globes. All such items were made in Nuremberg as well as other major centres like Antwerp for a variety of markets (Gallois, 70–131; Pilz II; Turner, 35–47). The ivory diptychs feature horizontal and vertical dials marked for several latitudes and different hour systems; tables of towns and their latitudes; wind roses; compasses marked with magnetic variation; and a range of computational devices such as lunar vovelles and epact tables.

The collation of such data seems relatively straightforward in our modern age of information technology. It is important to remember, however, that the extensive astronomical and navigational observations necessary to draw up tables and maps accurately had scarcely begun by the middle of the fifteenth century. Until the development of printing there were limitations to the possibility of comparing results of observations made on different occasions or at different locations (Eisenstein, 575–635).

68 Advertisement for
Regiomontanus's publishing house
BSB, Rar. 320, fol. 191ʳ.

Soon after his arrival in Nuremberg in 1471, Regiomontanus produced a list which announced his intention to publish both modern works on astronomy and mathematics and translations of the most important ancient scientific texts (fig. 68). In addition he advertised instruments and books on instruments available in his workshop (Zinner III, 163–236). Although Regiomontanus did not live long enough himself to implement all his plans, the potential for this kind of commercial production was soon fulfilled by others in Nuremberg, notably Bernhard Walther (fl. 1470–d. 1504).

Regiomontanus's involvement with astronomical reform had begun in 1450 when he first went to study with Georg Peurbach (1423–1461) at the University of Vienna. Over the next seven years the two collaborated on systematic astronomical observations, producing data which eventually appeared in Peurbach's *Eclipse Tables* of 1459 (printed in 1544) and in an improved version of Ptolemy's star catalogue in the *Epitome* of the *Almagest*. This was completed by Regiomontanus in early 1463, printed for the first time in Venice in 1496 (fig. 17), and appeared in numerous editions thereafter (fig. 69; see entries on Peurbach and Regiomontanus in *DSB*).

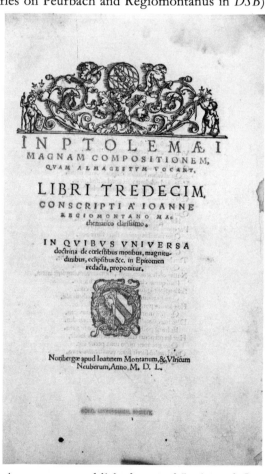

69 Title page
Johannes Regiomontanus, In Ptolemaei magnam compositionem, quam almagestum vocant, libri tredecim *(Nuremberg, 1550).*
RAS.

One work of which Regiomontanus published several Latin and German versions in his lifetime was his *Kalender* (Pilz II, 80–2). This was aimed at a general audience, containing information about saints' days, the rising and setting of the sun and the phases of the moon. A list of sixty-two places with their co-ordinates was also provided, so that the information might be applied to different locations. In addition, the *Kalender* contained woodcuts of several horological instruments which could be used by the reader. These included a nocturnal, a horary quadrant and a portable sundial adjustable according to latitude, now known as a Regiomontanus dial.

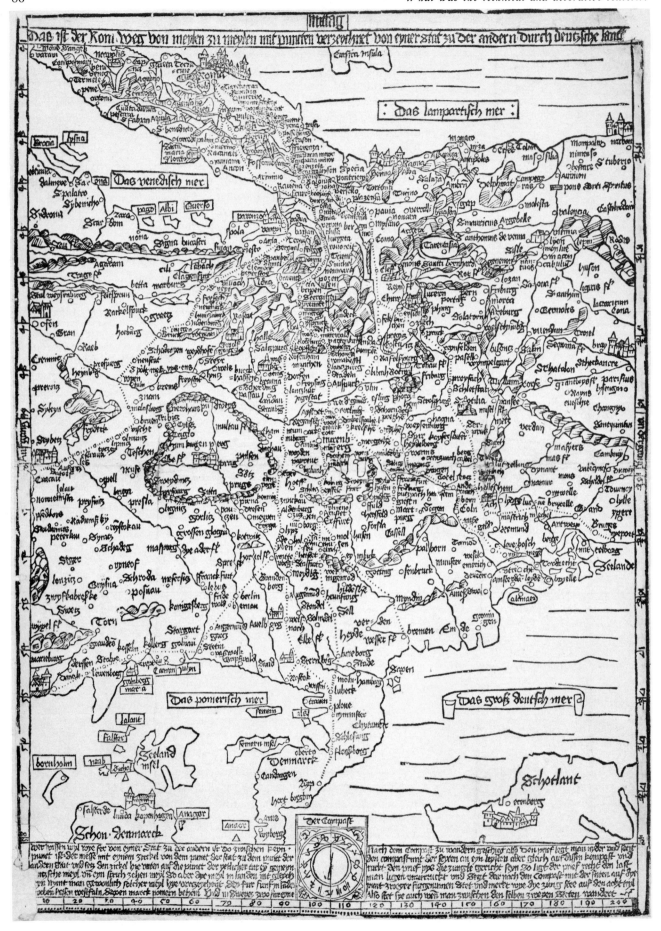

The close links between astronomy, cartography and the design of instruments are apparent from the work of Erhard Etzlaub, who first came to Nuremberg in 1484.   In the course of his career, Etzlaub applied himself to map making, surveying and the production of almanacs and calendars (Schnelbögl I & II).   Not only was he a medical practitioner, he was also innovative in the manufacture of portable sundials in the early sixteenth century.

Etzlaub's 'Rom Weg', printed from a woodcut made by Georg Glockendon around 1500, is the oldest surviving published map of Germany and central Europe.   It was intended for use by pilgrims travelling to Rome (fig. 70; Durand, 266–70; *History of Technology*, vol. 3, 534–5).   Different imprints of this map are extant in a number of European libraries.   They show the principal cities, topographical features and trade routes of an area lying between 58° and 41° latitude in a south-north orientation, and were designed for use with a compass dial.   Instructions how to use the map are included along with a representation of an instrument with a south-pointing needle marked for magnetic variation of about 10° E (see Taylor II).

Technical design of the diptychs

The introduction of a string gnomon adjustable to different latitudes together with a corresponding set of hour rings marked an important stage in the earliest development of the diptych dial.   It meant that the instrument would be an accurate time-piece in more than one location.   On the earliest known ivory diptychs no such features are present, but the wooden diptych of 1511, supposedly by Etzlaub, has a string-gnomon dial adjustable for a series of latitudes between 24° and 54° 30′, an unusually wide range.   The design of this instrument certainly reveals an affinity with the art of cartography.   On the outside of the upper leaf is a map of Europe and the Mediterranean oriented from south to north, while a scale of latitudes is inscribed in the margin.   The latitude of Mount Sinai and the southern and eastern coast of the Mediterranean are emphasized, which suggests that Etzlaub was looking for prospective buyers among merchants and pilgrims to Palestine (figs 55, 71).

70 'Rom-Weg' map of Europe by Erhard Etzlaub, woodcut by Georg Glockendon, c. 1500
The map is aligned south-north, showing a horizontal compass with south-pointing needle.
BL, Maps C. 2. a 7 (2).

71 Diptych dial in boxwood, attributed to Erhard Etzlaub, Nuremberg, 1511
Leaf 1a is engraved with a Mediterranean map. In order to minimize distortion in projecting the surface of a sphere on a plane, Etzlaub narrowed the space between the latitudes towards the south, thereby anticipating Mercator's projection by some fifty years.
GNM, WI 28. *(See also fig. 55).*

Tables of latitudes

Etzlaub's method of representing latitudes by means of a map is not found on any of the ivory diptychs. Information about latitudes, if contained on the dial, was presented in tabular form, resembling a printed list. On ivory instruments, this method seems more suitable than any attempt to reproduce a detailed map. That would have required considerable time and skill, neither of which could be afforded in bulk manufacture. On brass instruments, the process of engraving a map seems to have been easier. Examples of maps are found in some astronomical *compendia* made by Christoph Schissler (c. 1531–1608) of Augsburg (e.g. Bobinger, 29, 111–12). Lists of place names and latitude numbers were apparently much easier to replicate on the ivory sundials. A close study of the latitude tables and the calibration of hour lines on the instruments themselves has led to some interesting findings.

For example, on most sixteenth-century instruments with latitude tables, Nuremberg is represented as being at 49° (fig. 72). However, on later examples, Nuremberg is regularly assigned the latitude of 48° (Plate VI). The reason for this change seems to have been in order to place towns into standardized groups and to limit the number of latitudes shown. By this method of simplification, Nuremberg, Vienna, Augsburg and Paris – some of the major centres of Europe – were all considered to be at 48°.

72 Georg Hartmann, 1562
Leaf 2b with a table of thirty-four towns from 37° to 54° latitude, with Nuremberg marked for 49°.
Cat. 24. *(See also Plate II and fig. 14).*

The normal range for adjustable instruments was found to be for a selection of three to six latitudes between 42° and 54° (say, from Rome to Lübeck) with an attachment point at every third degree. On very large instruments the range is sometimes extended from 39° to 57° (Lisbon to Marienburg, now Malbork near Gdańsk) with as many as seven attachment points. In the same way the number of towns listed spans from anything between fifteen and a hundred, where the letters are so tiny that they can scarcely be read – a real feat of virtuoso craftsmanship (fig. 73).

The practice of standardizing latitudes is also revealed on the instruments with fixed-string gnomons. The most common method of deter-

73 Hans Troschel the younger, 1618
Seventy-two towns are listed in the table of latitudes on 1b. The lower leaf is decorated with scrollwork of acanthus leaves, cherubs, and two winged demi-figures which resemble those in figs 67 and 90.
Cat. 5. *(See also Plate XII).*

mining for which latitude a horizontal dial is intended can be briefly outlined. The tangent of the angle between the 12 o'clock and 3 o'clock lines equals the sine of the angle of latitude (Archinard, 6). However, it must be said that the present author found it difficult to measure the angles on the smallest instruments and to apply this formula with any great precision; the difference between hour line angles for 48° and 49°, for example, would in practice be virtually negligible.

With this proviso in mind, it can be stated that the calibration found on most of the fixed instruments was for approximately 48° latitude. The smallest diptychs made with layers of ivory and wood seem to be of this type (fig. 74). These could be used across most of central Europe.

74 Karner type, late 17th/early 18th century
The upper leaf is of ivory, the lower leaf is ivory with a wooden core.
Cat. 46.

However, some instruments of Nuremberg provenance are designed for different latitudes, which might suggest that they were commissioned. For example, Cat. 29 is calibrated for 51° 30′, suitable for Kassel, Antwerp or even London, while Cat. 48 has a fixed-string gnomon for about 56°, that of Copenhagen or Edinburgh. It must be noted that such a diptych was not necessarily restricted for use in a single latitude. It could also be combined with a universal equatorial dial, in which case a latitude table was also appropriate. Two horizontal compass dials found in London (Cat. 60, Cat. 61) appear to have been calibrated for approximately 51°, which suggests that they were actually produced with the English market in mind (see also Chapter seven).

Where did the compass-makers obtain their lists of latitudes? This question is not easily answered. They were certainly up to contemporary standards of accuracy. Variation in the choice of towns and even the latitude numbers among the instruments from different workshops suggests, however, that there was more than one source for them. The precise origins of these latitude tables cannot easily be determined, although a connection with the Ptolemaic tradition can be assumed (Table 8). Since its translation into Latin in the early fifteenth century, Ptolemy's *Geography* was the chief source for map co-ordinates until well into the seventeenth century (Durand, 12–13, 25–9). The work contained a set of tables of the latitudes and longitudes of over eight thousand places.

During the sixteenth century some modifications of Ptolemy's figures and new co-ordinates based on direct astronomical observation appeared both in new publications and in various editions of Ptolemy. The appearance of tables of latitudes and explanations of co-ordinates became familiar and commonplace in popular astronomical and geographical texts (fig. 75; Gallois, 97–100).

Although corrections and amendments to Ptolemy were in fact made long before this period, such information remained isolated and limited to a few manuscript sources until the advent of printing. For example, the latitude of Nuremberg was measured precisely to the minute (49° 27′) by visiting astronomers in 1427–28. These and other revised calculations for Vienna, Prague and elsewhere are found in fourteenth- and fifteenth-century manuscripts in Vienna (Durand, 42–5, 105–9). It was only through their publication that such figures were gradually incorporated into general circulation.

Regiomontanus took most of the tables in his *Kalender* and *Ephemerides* (1474) from Ptolemy, although his figures for Vienna and Nuremberg, for example, relied on new astronomical determinations (Gallois, 8–10, 243). Johannes Stöfler (1452–1531), a mathematician and philosopher at the University of Tübingen, included tables of co-ordinates in a number of his astronomical works such as the *Elucidatio fabricae ususque astrolabii* (Oppenheim, 1513). Stöfler mainly followed Regiomontanus, adding Basel, Tübingen and Ferrara to his list of towns. Yet his figures for places in North Africa and the Near East, for example, like those of Regiomontanus, were still based on Ptolemy (Gallois, 105–111, 245).

Sixteenth-century editions of Ptolemy also included additions and modifications to the table of co-ordinates. In 1514 Johannes Werner (1468–1522) published a translation at Nuremberg of the first book of Ptolemy, to which he added a detailed account of how to determine latitude correctly by measuring the altitude of the celestial pole (Gallois, 117–22). The Nuremberg patrician Willibald Pirckheimer (c. 1470–1530) published his new Latin version of Ptolemy's *Geography* in 1521 (Pilz II, 74). As Pirckheimer had access to Regiomontanus' papers, he included an attack by Regiomontanus on an earlier translation of

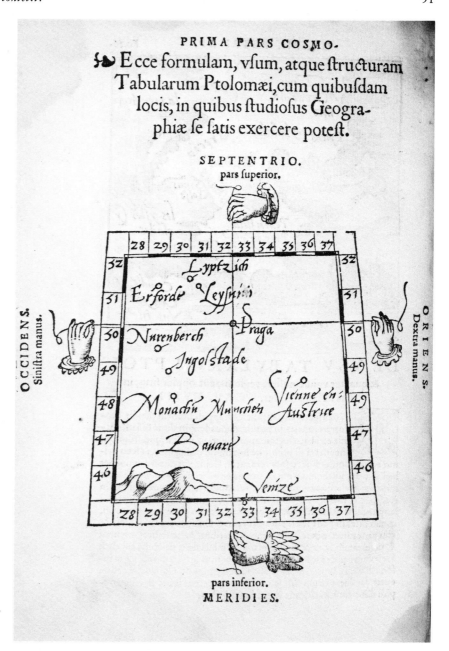

75 Explanation of geographical
co-ordinates based on Ptolemy
Peter Apian, Cosmographia *(Antwerp,*
1553), fol. 26ᵛ.
RAS.

Ptolemy in the appendix.   He also added several improved co-ordinates
for places that were taken from Regiomontanus' papers.

Hour lines and general layout

The person most likely to have provided technical designs for the Nuremberg ivory diptychs was Georg Hartmann, who, as already mentioned,
was active in Nuremberg after 1518 (Zinner I, 357–61; article in
DSB).   This conclusion is partly based on the existence of several prints
signed by Hartmann of diptychs for particular latitudes dated between
1535 and 1553 (see figs 59, 64; Zinner I, 363–6).   Although none of these
designs is found exactly reproduced on any one ivory diptych, they give
the impression that Hartmann kept close contact with both engravers and
instrument makers (figs 76 and 77).

Some indication of collaboration can be gleaned from a close study of two instruments in the exhibition. One signed by Hieronymus Reinmann (fig. 52) and one signed by Hartmann himself (Plate II, fig. 72) show a strong resemblance to one another. Both have the same large sun face on one leaf, the compass bowl of each is marked with the name of the eight winds, and the use of green and red colouring is comparable. Another striking similarity is the selection of place names in their latitude tables; the spelling and even the lettering of these look remarkably alike. It

76 Engraving of inner leaves of diptych calibrated for 49° 27' (the latitude of Nuremberg) by Georg Hartmann, 1553.
The lower leaf of the dial is calibrated for Babylonian and common hours. Day length is marked by zodiac symbol and by saints' days.
BSB, MS Rar. 434, fol. 49.

77 Hans Troschel, 1580
Leaf 2a has a string-gnomon dial calibrated for common hours, Italian and Babylonian hours and day length. Inscribed 'die blaeben zal ist der tagleng bedeiten die zirkel' (the blue number is the day length represent[ed by] the circles); 'krichisch tevtsch vnd welsche stvndt' (i.e. Babylonian, common and Italian hours).
Cat. 28.

78 Johann Gebhart, 1561
One of several diptychs of similar design produced around 1560. Compare figs 46 and 52.
Cat. 25.

would seem that they were actually made by the same maker or workshop. To lend weight to this argument, it can be noted that an ivory diptych of 1562 in the British Museum signed by Hartmann is also stamped with the Reinmann maker's mark of a crown (Ward, 35). In theory at least, Hartmann would not have been allowed to use the mark himself. It is more likely that he commissioned compass-makers such as Reinmann for the ivory diptychs that he designed and sold, just as he would have employed brass workers for the astrolabes that were produced under his name (Turner, 39–40).

Changing fashions in technical design

In fact, other instruments in this exhibition bear evidence that during the 1550s and 1560s the diptych design shown in figure 52 was particularly fashionable (figs 46, 78). They each have an equatorial dial, a fixed string gnomon for the vertical and horizontal dials, a table of towns and latitudes, and the names of the eight winds inscribed in the compass bowl.

From the late 1570s another type of layout was favoured by the Hans Tuchers and the elder Hans Troschel (Plate VIII; fig. 57). The equatorial dial seems to have fallen from favour at this date, while the use of an adjustable string gnomon was more popular. It is also during this period that the wind rose and lunar volvelle first made their appearance on diptychs, accompanied by inscriptions explaining their use. Unfortunately there is no indication who might have provided the designs for these particular instruments. The earliest representations of this style of diptych dial are engravings in the *Descriptio et usus viatorii et horologii solaris* (Nuremberg, 1597), published by the book and instrument seller Levinius Hulsius (see above, fig. 22).

On the basis of instruments seen by the author, epact tables seem to have first been added to instruments by Paul Reinmann around the turn of the century (fig. 79). They are found on later diptychs by makers such as Michael Lesel, Conrad and Jacob Karner. A demonstration of how designs must also have been reproduced without any technical understanding in the compass-makers' workshops is given by the epact tables on instruments by Thomas Tucher and his son, Joseph (e.g. fig. 80). These always begin with the same pair of numbers – 17/7 – regardless of the year when the diptych was made. In addition, the outer circle

79 Paul Reinmann, 1608
Reinmann seems to have been the first to have added epact tables to his diptychs; the example shown is relatively late. The epact numbers are those in the two outermost circles inscribed 'EPACTA IVLIANI ANNO 1608 IST', beginning with 23 for 1608, and 'EPACTA GREGORII ANNO 1608 IST', beginning with 13. The next two circles are time-correction scales of hours (S = Stunden) and minutes (M) which allow a more accurate conversion between lunar and solar time when using the lunar volvelle. The spandrels are decorated with arabesque foliage.
Cat. 51.

80 Joseph Tucher, before 1644
A characteristic feature of diptychs made by Joseph Tucher and his father Thomas is the incorrect table of epacts. The names 'epagta gregori' [sic] and 'epagta iullana' [sic] should be reversed for the numbers to be correct. Since the tables always begin with 17/7 (for the years either 1621 or 1640) the epact tables do not seem to offer a reliably accurate method of dating these later Tucher instruments.
Cat. 53. *(See also fig. 83).*

of numbers is always marked as 'Gregorian' epacts, the inner one as 'Julian' epacts, when in fact the names should be reversed. Another repeated error on dials by the younger Tuchers is the incorrect numbering put on hour lines marked for unequal or planetary hours, which are inscribed 4–12–8 rather than 1–12 (Plate yy). These observations about stylistic differences among the instruments lead naturally to a consideration of their ornamental features.

Ornamental design of the diptychs

The decoration found on the ivory sundials consists principally of punched symbols (letters and numbers, zodiac signs, motifs of sun, moon, stars, etc.), and engravings, both iconic and non-iconic (fig. 81). On the basis of these details, together with differences in technical design already mentioned, the instruments in the exhibition can be roughly grouped into categories. This method of classification offers a guide to the identification and provisional dating of some unsigned instruments. It is, of course, subject to further refinement and correction. For example, one means of refinement that has not yet been fully exploited is the comparison of the punch marks for letters and numbers. This technique might provide some answers to the following questions. Can an unsigned instrument be identified by its lettering and numbering alone? Is it possible to show that a particular maker changed his punches at any point in his career? Were punches sometimes transferred from father to son or nephew? In order for an investigation of this type to be successful, it

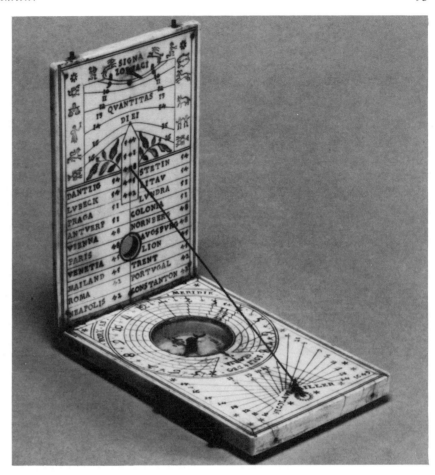

81 Nicolaus Miller, 1649
The zodiac symbols, numbers and letter punches are particularly clear on this diptych.
Cat. 16.

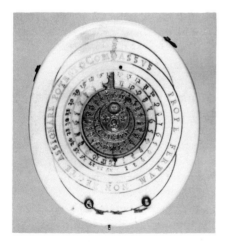

82 Hans Tucher, 1600
Leaf 2b showing lunar volvelle with a stamped and pierced brass disc, inscribed 'COMPASSVS PROPE FERRVM NON RECTE ASSIGNARE POTEST' (near iron the compass cannot point properly). The letter 'P' in 'compassus' has been punched over a letter 'O' used by mistake.
Cat. 19.

would be necessary to examine a great many diptychs in as many collections as possible.

Two groups of sixteenth-century instruments have already been identified in the previous sub-section. The first of these includes diptychs of the 1550s and 1560s by Johann Gebhart, Hieronymus Reinmann and Georg Hartmann, while the second comprises most diptychs by the early Tuchers and Troschels made between about 1570 and 1610.

The decoration of this second type consists almost entirely of Latin and German words in Roman and Gothic script (black-letter), with the colouring usually limited to red and black. The most common injunction on the Tucher dials is 'wen ich kampast recht sol weisen so richt mich nicht nahet bei eissen', or the Latin equivalent 'COMPASSVS PROPE FERRVM NON RECTE ASSIGNARE POTEST' (fig. 82). Further inscriptions are sometimes used to explain how to adjust the string gnomon for different latitudes and to read the correct time from the dial.

Mottoes are also an important form of inscription. Of the sixteenth-century makers Hans Troschel used them most frequently, while the Hans Tuchers apparently did not use them at all. Most makers of the seventeenth century added mottoes to at least some of their dials (Hyatt). These were drawn from a common stock of pithy sayings found on all kinds of sundials and time-telling devices, as well as appearing in innumerable books of emblems. Alluding to the passing of time and the brevity of life, they convey moral and religious sentiments:

Hora fugit mors venit (the hour flies, death approaches)
Tempus sumptus est preciosissimus (time taken up is most precious)
Monstro viam perge securus (I show the way, go on securely)
Soli Deo gloria (glory to God alone)

Two main groups of seventeenth-century instruments are also discernible. The practice of limiting decoration to words, simple motifs such as the sun, moon and stars and geometrical patterns is characteristic for the first group. Like those of the early Tucher and Troschel instruments, the decorations of these medium- and small-sized diptychs consist mainly of punched motifs with a limited range of mottoes, and use red, black and occasionally blue colouring. Most instruments by Jacob, Georg and Melchior Karner fall into this category, while examples by Hans Troschel the younger, Leonhart and Nicolaus Miller are also found. The Karners particularly favoured the snowflake, quatrefoil and eight-pointed star motifs (fig. 105, motif numbers 11, 14, 17).

The other identifiable group, of which most were made in the second quarter of the seventeenth century, seems to have been influenced by pattern books. These diptychs, which usually have latitude tables, are highly ornamented with engravings of foliage, fruit and flowers, animals, putti and cherub heads and vignettes. The colours used include orange, green, blue and sometimes gilt as well as red and black. Examples of this type were produced by Michael Lesel, Leonhart Miller, Thomas and Joseph Tucher.

One group which departs radically from the typology just developed includes small diptychs in the shape of a book with clasps. The examples shown in the exhibition were obviously produced concurrently with other types between about 1585 and 1620 (Cats. 29–33). Two are signed by Hans Troschel (Plate I; fig. 117), one has the crown mark of Paul Reinmann (fig. 118), the next is stamped with the mark of Conrad Karner (Plate XIII) while another looks very much as if by the same hand (fig. 8). The outside of each leaf is carefully ornamented with an engraved shield of arms of a family, figure of a saint or similar themes.

The range and variety of Paul Reinmann's ivory instruments is so great that they effectively form a group of their own. Further sub-classification of his *oeuvre* would be desirable, but cannot be attempted in this study. It was Reinmann who first extensively adopted the practice of ornamenting the diptychs with fine decorative borders and engraved figures and scenes which were apparently taken from contemporary pattern books, prints or manuscripts of Biblical scenes and emblem books. His most productive years lay between about 1597 and 1608.

83 Thomas Tucher, before 1645
Apart from the incorrect table of epacts shown here, another characteristic feature of instruments by Thomas Tucher is the use of cast gilt brass spandrels and clasps similar to the decoration used on book bindings. The clusters of fruit, flowers and leaves resemble those shown in fig. 91. Cat. 36. *(See also Plate VII).*

Identification and dating

On the basis of these preliminary observations it seems possible to determine whether an instrument with a Tucher snake mark, for example, was made by Thomas rather than either of the Hans Tuchers. Those of Thomas are elaborately decorated with scrollwork of fruit, flowers and leaves and are often in the shape of a book. They also incorporate characteristic designs such as the triple-ringed 'globe' figure and cast gilt brass spandrels which also serve as feet (Plate VII, fig. 83).

Instead of simply ascribing all instruments stamped with a crown to Reinmann or his workshop, a similar distinction on the grounds of style can be made between those of Reinmann and Lesel. The style and colouring of the ornamentation used in the late 1620s contrasts clearly with that of the earlier period. The difference between the Reinmann/Lesel mark and the crown mark of Nicolaus Miller should also aid identification (fig. 104).

A few general remarks can now be made about some of the main forms of ornament found on the diptychs, and their use on other objects of the period.

PLATE XII: Hans Troschel
the younger, 1618, 2b
Cat. 5.

PLATE XIII: Conrad Karner, 1b/2a
Cat. 31.

PLATE XIV: Paul Reinmann,
1598/9, 1a
Cat. 1.

PLATE XV: Paul Reinmann, 1598/9,
2b
Cat. 1.

Iconic images

The figures used to adorn the sundials are usually either religious/moral, amorous/erotic, exotic, or a combination of these types.   Images such as the Virgin and saints were perhaps designs that would have been specifically requested by the purchaser.   One large diptych from the Reinmann workshop is engraved with the Woman of the Apocalypse (*Revelation* 12.1), standing above a crescent moon (fig. 62).   Although no examples are shown in this catalogue, Reinmann used scenes from the Nativity on several diptychs (e.g. BM, No. 17 11–15 14, with the adoration of the shepherds; GNM, WI 154, with the Annunciation on one side and the adoration of the shepherds on the other).

The thin dividing-line between morality and eroticism was exploited to good effect (Byrne, 17).   A diptych of 1598, probably by Paul Reinmann, is a fine example of such practice (Cat. 1, see Plates XIV, XV).   Two famous women of virtue from the Old Testament are portrayed.   Judith is holding the gruesome head of Holophernes which she has just severed, while Susanna sits naked in her bath. Susanna's struggle with the elders, which was already a favourite theme among painters and sculptors, became a popular erotic image on pocket watches of the later seventeenth and eighteenth centuries (fig. 84; Landes, figure 28; Henkel & Schöne, cols 1855–7).

Courting couples accompanied by musicians were obviously a fashionable theme in 1602.   Almost identical engravings are found on three Reinmann instruments of this date.   One is shown in this exhibition (fig. 124).   The others are in the Museo Poldi-Pezzoli, Milan (Milan, 20, 45) and in the Metropolitan Museum of Art, New York (Chandler & Vincent I, 161).   The theme is one which was already favoured by south German gunsmiths in the elaborate ornamentation of pistols and hunting rifles (fig. 85).

A very common image on the diptychs in this exhibition is the so-called *memento mori* or reminder of death.   Like many mottoes also found on the dials, these formed part of the popular *vanitas* tradition of the sixteenth and early seventeenth centuries (Henkel & Schöne, cols 997–8, 1343–4, 1471–3).   Paintings, sculptures, engravings and many other artefacts of the period incorporate didactic and moral symbols of this nature.   In this exhibition there are several instruments which portray similar representations of one particular emblem: a naked putto or androgyne figure

84 Striking gold watch, by Daniel Delandes, London, late 17th century
The casting is ornamented with Susanna and the elders.
Christie's sale catalogue, 31.1.67.

85 *Radschlosspistole*, Nuremberg, late 16th century
Ornamented with hunting scene including courting couples and musicians.
BNM, W 1496.

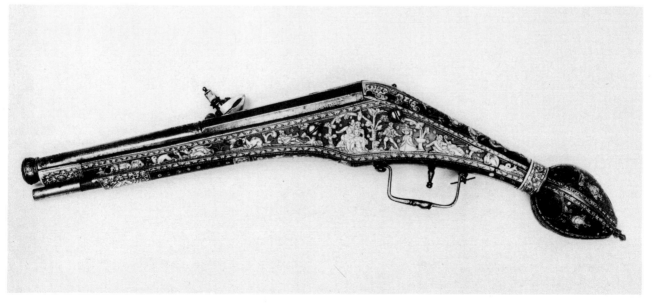

86 Paul Reinmann, 1578
The upper leaf has a memento mori *of
a reclining putto with his arm resting on a
skull. Compare Plate I, in which an hour-
glass is also included in the emblem.*
Cat. 34.

reclines on a mound, with a skull and hour glass nearby (e.g. Plate I, fig.
86). Together these symbolize the passing of time and the inevitability
of death.

The heads of blowing putti are frequently used on the diptychs to
represent the winds, in much the same way as they are used on maps and
globes. Examples of different wind punches used in the compass bowls
or on the outer leaves by various makers are given in figure 105, motifs
1–6. Stylized engravings of the four winds are also found on the outside
leaves of some diptychs, notably those of Joseph Tucher (fig.
80). Alternatively, the heads are those of winged cherubs (fig. 87).

Leaves

The most common subject for ornament, not only on these instruments,
but on many other decorated artefacts of the Renaissance, was
undoubtedly the leaf (Byrne, 51). Leaves can be varied, easily stylized,
arranged to fill any awkward space and combined with other
motifs. Many of the most popular shapes for leaves and their arrangement were initially Near Eastern in origin, probably introduced via
Venice, and by the early seventeenth century they had become generic
(J. Evans, 163–77).

At least three main types of leaf can be identified on the diptychs, usually
arranged in the form of tendrils arising from a centre point and scrolling
symmetrically to the left and right. A few examples of each can be
mentioned. The fist-shaped leaf, which is of Italian, early Renaissance

87 Thomas Tucher, before 1645
*The leaf is ornamented with wide borders
of stylized bound wreaths, and in each
spandrel is a cherub head. The volvelle is
for converting between common and either
Italian or Babylonian hours.*
Cat. 37.

88 Flower sprays, including pinks, by Paul Flindt, c. 1593
Dotted-print or stipple engraving (Punzenstiche).
© The Board of Trustees of the Victoria & Albert Museum, London, E. 4233–1910.

origin, is found on two early Karner instruments (Plate XIII; fig. 125), the blade-shaped leaf is represented on several Miller diptychs (Plate III; figs. 53, 81), while the hook-shaped leaf is found most frequently on instruments by the later Tuchers (e.g. Plates VI, IX).   Elaborate scrollwork with acanthus leaves and winged demi-figures is used on the large diptych by Hans Troschel the younger (Plate XII), and several examples of arabesque foliage are on pieces by Paul Reinmann and his workshop (e.g. fig. 79).

Flowers

Flowers constitute another current form of ornament found among the minor arts of the early seventeenth century (J. Evans, 62–3, 72–9).   Of those flowers which can be identified, the two most common types on the diptychs are the rose, sometimes used as the symbol of the Virgin, and the pink, the symbol of bethrothal (e.g. figs 8, 62).   Examples of pinks were illustrated by Paul Flindt in one of his pattern sheets of about 1593 (fig. 88).   Another of his designs, sprays of flowers in an ornate two-handled urn, is echoed in a diptych by Paul Reinmann of around 1600 (fig. 89, Plate IV).   Tiny snails, like those on Flindt's pattern, are also incorporated into the vignette on the upper part of the same leaf.

89 Ornamental urn with flower
spray, by Paul Flindt, c. 1593
Dotted-print or stipple engraving
(Punzenstiche).
© The Board of Trustees of the
Victoria & Albert Museum, London,
E. 3904–1910.

Fruit and vegetables

Clusters of fruit and vegetables were a form of decoration which origi-
nated in Flemish strapwork of the mid-sixteenth century but soon became
widespread.   These clusters usually included stylized representations of
burst pomegranates and marrow-like vegetables surrounded with foliage
and sometimes flowers (J. Evans, 170–2; Irmscher, 143).   Variations of
this design are found in prints by Paul Flindt and Hieronymus Bang (fig.
90, see also figs 66, 67).   It was a motif which first seems to have been
used by compass-makers around 1627; two almost identical examples are
those by Leonhart Miller (fig. 122) and Michael Lesel (Cat. 11).   Similar
designs, also coloured in green and orange, are found on instruments
assumed to be by Thomas Tucher (fig. 83).

Birds, animals etc.

Like flowers, birds were typically added to foliage decoration for variety
and interest (Byrne, 51).   Several of the stylized birds found in the Bang
and Sibmacher prints resemble examples found on diptychs by Lesel and
Thomas Tucher (fig. 91; Plate VI, Cat. 56).   Birds could also have a
symbolic function; the pelican feeding her young from her own breast
symbolized the Redemption, for example (Plate I).

Running hounds and deer (Plate IX; fig. 12) were also favoured motifs on inlaid gun-stocks made in Nuremberg and other south German centres in the first quarter of the seventeenth century (figs 85, 92). The hunting scene in linear form, which had adorned French manuscripts of the fourteenth and fifteenth centuries, had by the late sixteenth century become even more popular owing to the engravings of the 'small masters' such as Georg Pencz (c. 1500–1550), and Virgil Solis (J. Evans, 54). There was obviously a time lag before ornament of this kind was eventually transferred to artefacts such as guns and sundials.

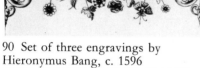

90 Set of three engravings by
Hieronymus Bang, c. 1596
GNM, K 12478, K 12479, K 12480.

91 Set of four engravings by Johann Sibmacher, c. 1600 GNM, K 23088.

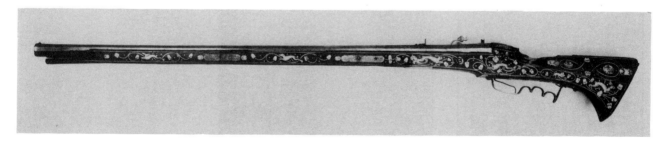

92 *Radschlossbüchse*, German, end of
16th century
BNM, W 828.

TABLE 8: List of Latitudes

Source\Town	Lübeck	London	Prague	Nuremberg	Paris	Vienna	Venice	Rome	Constantinople	Lisbon
Modern Latitude	53°52′	51°30′	50°05′	49°27′	48°52′	48°13′	45°26′	41°53′	41°02′	38°44′
Ptolemy, *Geography*	—	54°	—	—	48°10′	46°50′	44°10′	41°40′	—	40°15′
Regiomontan, *Kalender* (1474)	56°	—	50°	49°	48°	48°	45°	42°	46°	41°
J. Stöfler, *Elucidatio* (1524)	—	54°	50°	49°27′	48°	45°	45°	42°	47°	41°
Cat. 22 (1559) H. Reinmann	52°	—	52°	49°	48°	48°	45°	42°	—	39°
Cat. 24 (1562) G. Hartmann	52°	52°	50°	49°	48°	48°	45°	42°	42°	—
Cat. 17 (1567) H. Tucher	55°	—	50°	49°	48°	48°	45°	42°	43°	40°
Cat. 55 (1603) P. Reinmann	54°	—	50°	49°	48°	48°	45°	42°	42°	40°
Cat. 51 (1608) P. Reinmann	54°	51°	51°	48°	48°	—	—	42°	42°	39°
Cat. 39 (1627) L. Miller	54°	51°	51°	48°	—	48°	45°	42°	42°	—
Cat. 47 (1632) C. Karner	54°	51°	51°	—	—	48°	45°	42°	—	—
Cat. 9 (1639) J. Karner	—	51°	51°	48°	48°	48°	45°	42°	—	—
Cat. 16 (1649) N. Miller	54°	51°	51°	48°	48°	48°	45°	42°	42°	—
Cat. 3 (c. 1640) T. Tucher	—	54°	—	—	54°	—	42°	42°	—	—
Cat. 40 (c. 1640) J. Tucher	—	—	54°	—	—	48°	—	42°	—	—

CHAPTER SEVEN

What was the market for them?

The question of whom the ivory diptychs were made for is part of a much broader enquiry into the dynamics of an economic and social network which bound together maker, retailer, buyer and user. A close examination of the ornament of the dials themselves has yielded some helpful data which have been supplemented by archival material.

Commissioned instruments

One of the best indications that an instrument was made for a particular individual or family is the incorporation of a shield of arms into its design. Unfortunately, these are usually difficult to identify, since they require familiarity with heraldry. One example where the arms have been identified is by Paul Reinmann in the British Museum (no. 71 11–15 14; Ward, 37). The arms of the Holzschuher family of Nuremberg are incorporated into the decoration of the vertical string-gnomon dial on the upper leaf. On an instrument by Hans Troschel (Cat. 33, Plate I), probably dating from the end of the sixteenth century, an armorial device is found on the outside of the lower leaf. As yet the family has not been identified, although it is likely to have been from Nuremberg.

In this exhibition the only example of an instrument which has the name of the recipient on it is Cat. 26 (fig. 93). The inscription on the gilt brass plate on the top of the inner leaf reads:

> M. V. D. Thomae Loeffelholtz. patricio Norib: cons: in Septu: senatum electo. devotae gratulatio: ergo. d.d. christianus heide Anno .M.D. L. X. IX. octobris. XXVII.

(For the Master, the Right Honourable Thomas Loeffelholtz, patrician of the Nuremberg Council, the elect to the Council of the Seven Lords Elders, loyal congratulations: therefore Christian Heide gave the gift in the year 1569, on the 27th of October.)

Why did Christian Heiden produce an instrument for Thomas Loeffelholtz in 1569? The documents show that Loeffelholtz (1525–1575) was a member of a distinguished Nuremberg patrician family. He joined the city council in 1554 and in 1565 became an 'elder Mayor' (*alter Bürgermeister*). The Council of the Septemviri (*Sieben Herren Älteren*) was the most senior body in the city council. The seven members, elected out of the group of elder Mayors, were responsible for all aspects of financial and foreign policy of the city.

What could be more natural than to mark the occasion of Loeffelholtz's appointment with the presentation of a luxury gift, an object of beauty that would also be useful to the recipient? Like a gold watch today, an ivory sundial, with particularly elegant fittings of gilt brass, could function both practically and symbolically. An almost identical instrument of the same year is found in the Science Museum, London (Inv. 1952–231). This is inscribed with the name of Gabriel Nützell, and the donor was once again Heiden. Nützell was another member of the city council who was elected

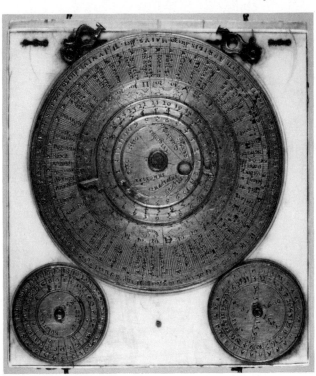

93 Christian Heiden, 1569
*This is the diptych which Heiden dedicated
to Thomas Loeffelholtz; the inscription is
on the inside upper leaf.*
Cat. 26.

in 1547 and died in 1576. The owners of these particular diptychs were
from the highest echelons of Nuremberg society.

There are a number of other surviving instruments, not only ivory
diptychs, that were made for high-ranking individuals by Christian Heiden. Whether Heiden actually made the diptychs himself or had them
produced by a compass-maker is open to question. Heiden, born in
Nuremberg in 1526, studied in Leipzig and Wittenberg, where his teacher
was the reformer Philip Melanchthon. Heiden became a schoolmaster in
1556 and subsequently a teacher of mathematics at the Nuremberg Gym-
nasium in 1564. In the Dresden Salon there is a brass horizontal compass
sundial which Heiden presented to Melanchthon in 1553. A smaller,
gilded brass compass sundial attributed to Heiden in the Kassel Lan-
desmuseum is engraved with the coat-of-arms of the Landgrave of
Hesse. Of particular interest is the ivory diptych dial with gilt brass and
silver accessories made for Emperor Maximilian II in 1571, now in the
Vienna Kunsthistorische Museum. Although it is initialled by Heiden,
the maker's mark on the underside of the lower leaf is that of Hans Tucher,
a crowned snake. This suggests that Tucher could have made the instrument to Heiden's specifications or that they worked in collaboration
(Zinner I, 369–71). It seems unlikely that Heiden himself ever was a
member of the compass-makers' craft.

Evidence that the work of Nuremberg compass-makers had already
found favour with the Emperor is found in a letter to him of 19 June
1568. A passage refers to a payment of 12 Rhenish guilders made by the
Emperor to the compass-maker Hieronymus Reinmann for a sundial. Unfortunately the size and type of the instrument, which would
provide some idea of its relative cost, are not known, but the dial would
certainly have been of the highest quality and craftsmanship (Zinner I,
484–5).

A similar pattern of producing commissioned instruments for high-
standing patrons is found in the work of Georg Hartmann. Hartmann
produced a compass sundial in the form of a cross for Melanchthon around
1542. In 1544 Duke Albrecht of Prussia ordered a range of different

Der Preißwürdigen Ehren-Zunfft / des Handwercks der Circkel-Schmiede: Als selbige ihren Dantz-Auffzug hielten am Tag Jacobi / so da war der 25. Julii 1681. Dem Löblichen Handwerck zu einem Ehrn-Andencken / entworffen und in Kupffer-Bildnis vorgestellet und übergeben von Thomas Hirschman Kupfferstechern in Nürnberg allhier.

Ist etwas rühmens werth / und wol verdient zu loben /
Von hohen Alterthum / und schönen Künstlers-Proben /
Ist etwas / daß der Welt zu hohen Nutz gereicht /
Und sich in alle Ding / bedient zu seyn erzeigt.
Ist was / so ist es das / was Tubal Cain weiset /
Von deme man die Kunst / des Eisen-Werckes preiset /
Als der die Meister-Kron dergleichen Künstler hies /
Und seinen klugen Geist / der Welt zur Nachfolg wies:
Daß sie durch Sinnlichkeit sich gleiches solten üben
Den nimmer müden Fleiß der Kunst-Werck zu belieben.
Damit der theure Ruhm des Meisters nicht vergeh /
Besonders mehr und mehr / Preiß gipffle / nach der Höh.
Ihr seyds / Ihr werthes Volck / und Ehren-Zunfft-Genossen /
Die von dem Künstler-Stamm / des Tubal Cains sprossen /
Man nennet Euch mit Recht / vom Circkel Circkelschmied /
Als von der Eisen-Kunst / das Kunst-belobste Glied.
Dann / laßt die schöne Kunst / die Erde auszumessen /
So da Geographi der Griche nannt vordessen;
Laßt den Archimedes / und Dädalus herfür /
Mit ihrem Bau-Geröth / und Architectur-Zier /
Laßt Dürer und Apell / zusamt dem Kranach kommen /
Wer hat der Sternen Stand iemahlen wahr genommen /
Daß er des Circkels doch nicht must benöthigt seyn?
Womit er Ziel und Maß / nach Ordnung richtet ein.
Hieraus erhellet schon / was Lob euch will geziemen /
Ihr würden-werthes Volck! wer wolte euch nicht rühmen /
Nach eurer Hände Werck / und Kunst belobten Stand /
Ihr gehet allen ja mit euren Thun zur Hand /
Der / so der Globen-Kunst / und Wissenschaft verstehet /
Wie sich die Erden Rund zusamt dem Himmel drehet /
Wie dis und ienes Land von andern sey entfernt /
Wie hoch dis Sternen-Licht / noch über jenem sternt.
Der Schreiner / Zimmerman / Mahl / Maurer und Bild...
Der Arithmeticus / und grosse Schiff-Erbauer /
Der Drechs... s / der kluge Ir...mer /
Die geben Eurem Werck / dem Circel die Ehr /
Wie vielmehr denen dann / die solchen künstlich machen /
Samt vielen andern Zeug und nutzbarn Handwercks-Sachen /
Wo ist ein Instrument / und Werckzeug ie zusehn /
Das nicht durch eure Hand und Arbeit müsse gehn?
Der Treponir-Gezeug / den da der Kunst-Artzt brauchet /
Die Stoß-Seeg / Maisel auch der Spadel / so ihm tauget /
Und was dergleichen mehr / von Handwercks Eisen zeuch /
Gilt Euch Ihr Künstler-Volck zu machen alles gleich.
Von Euch ist sonderbar / und rühmens-werth zu mercken:
Ohn Euch ist alles nichts / wer kan ohn Werckzeug wercken.
Ihr zieret und vermehrt / mit Wercken alles Land /
Ihr seyd der Handwercks-Kunst Anfang und erste Hand.
Der Schlosser und der Schmied / Schrein / Drechsler und Barbier /
Der Gold-und Kupfferschmied / der Drat-und Scheiben-Zieher /
Der Blätter und was mehr bedarf des Handwercks Zeug /
Diß alles werthe Freund / kan nicht entrahten Euch.
Wie solt dan Euer Ruhm / nicht über alle gehen /
Wie soltet ihr dann nicht zu vörderst billig stehen?

Wo sind nicht in der Welt die Circkel-Schmied beliebt /
Wer ists Ihr werthes Volck! der euch nicht Ehre giebt?
Wie manches Kronen-Haupt / hat euer Werck belobet /
In Franckreich / Dänien / seyd Ihr auch Kunst geprobet /
Was schöne Zug-Werck / sind nicht worden zu bereit /
Die manchen Königs Hoff / belustet und erfreut?
Die raren Wasserkunst / die da zu vielen Nutzen /
Und selbst das Element des Feuers übertrutzen /
Sind eurer Hände-Werck / und dienen Stadt und Land /
Dardurch Ihr Künstler-Freund / ist Euer Ruhm bekant.
Und wie? was sag ich viel / solt ich mich unterstehen /
In euren hohen Ruhm / noch weiter fortzugehen /
So wären zweymahl Sechs / gebang mir von thun /
Demnach so halt ich ein und schweige billig nun /
Von solchen Lob Gefall / mich heist was anders reden /
Es hat der schöne Zug / den jüngst die Zunfft-Freund thäten /
Der werthen Circkelschmied / nicht wen'ger Lobs verdient /
Drei Ein Hoch Edler Raht / dem Handwerck Gnad vergünt
Die wohlerbaute Hütt / und grün-gezierte Läuben /
So billig unerwähnt / und unbelobt nicht bleiben.
Daran ein Freud-Gemüth sich erbarlich ergötzt /
Und auch der danckbar Will / sein Denckmal beygesetzt /
In wohl-gemeinten Reim und etlich Dichter-Zeilen /
Die Ursach des Gebäus / dem Leser mitzutheilen.
Es gieng der schöne Dantz / so Sitten-artig ab /
Daß er der jungen Welt / ein Erbars Beyspiel gab /
Man hörte keine Klag / noch widriges erweisen /
Und kurz: es kunte recht / ein Erbrer Auffzug heissen /
So ist dann alles wohl und löblich nun vollend't?
Ja / zwar es hat der Dan... ...
Und wird auch nimmer Euch / Ihr Ehren-Volck zertraten /
So lang Ihr Euch befleißt / so erbar feiner Sinnen /
Und schöne Ordnung liebt / demnach so wünsch ich Glück /
Daß alles Euer Thun / sich ferner also schickt /
Zu hohen Ruhm und Ehr / und allen wol Erachen /
So lang das Circkel-Rund der Erde wird bestehen /
So lang ein Circkelschmied / der Nöris ist bekant /
So lang man lieben wird / die schöne Künstler-Hand /
So lang das Sonnen-Rad / ümrennt die Erben-Scheiben /
So lang soll Euer Ruhm / auch unverlöschlich bleiben /
Dis wünsch't ein guter Freund / aus guter Künstler-Lieb.
Der dieses Lob-Gedicht / zu euren Ehren schrieb /
Laßt euch beliebig seyn / ihm Gegen-Gunst zu weisen /
Es hat was er gethan / die Ehre ihm geheissen /
Und ist so ferner noch zu eurn Diensten gewend /
Indessen aber nimmt / die Ruhm-Red hier ein END.

NB: Die Reime so an der Hütte sind gewesen.
1. GOtt zu Ehren allezeit /
Einen Hoch Edlen Raht / zur Danckbarkeit /
Sind wir bereit /
Wegen unsers Dangs zu jeder Zeit.
2. Freuet euch und saget GOtt Danck /
Der noch erhelt den Handwercks-Stand /
Der Nutzen bringt der Stadt und Land.
GOtt erhalt auch ferner alle Zeit /
Alle ehrsam redliche Handwercks-Leut.
3. Der Circkel schwebt all Künsten ob /

Bey allen Künstlern hat ers Lob /
Stern / Kugel / und dergleichen Sachen /
Kan man nicht ohn den Circkel machen /
Feld-Messer und die mit Stücken schiessen /
Den Circkel die auch brauchen müssen /
Auch hat der Circkel sonsten Preiß /
Bey allen die machen ein Werck mit Fleiß /
So man auch den Dantz soll preissen /
Nur richtig und erbar läst uns erweisen /
So einer soll von Mittel schreiten /
So muß er seine Straf kum leiden.

PLATE XVI: Procession of the Divider-smiths on 25 July 1681
Nuremberg, Stadtgeschichtliche Museen.

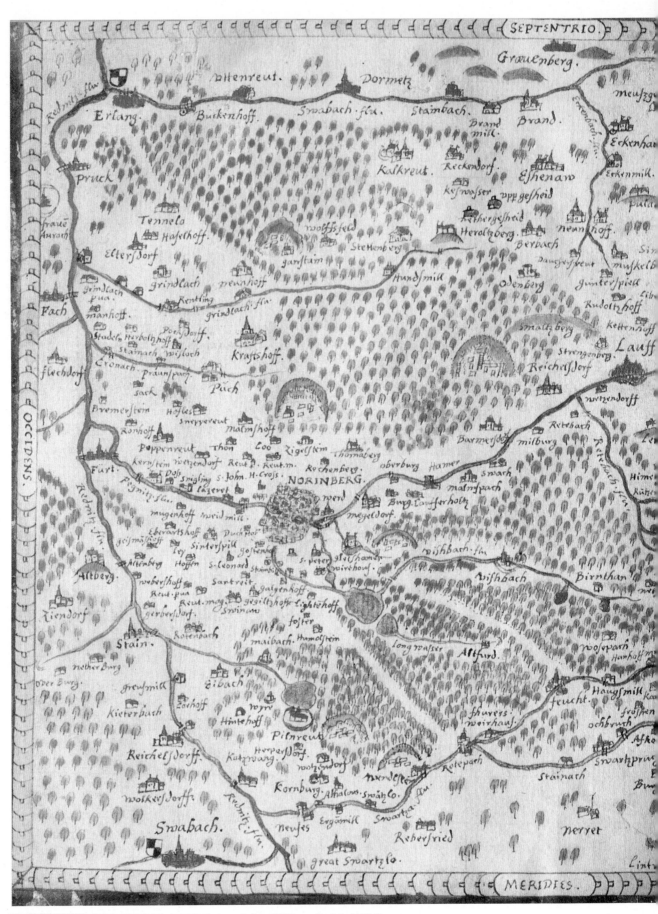

PLATE XVII: 'The Territory of Norinberg', by William Smith (1594)
Nuremberg, Stadtbibliothek, Nor.H. 1142. Photograph by Foto Hilbinger GmbH,
Schwaig-Behringersdorf.

THE
TERRITORY
OF
NORINBERG.

Scala
Milliarium
Germanicorum.

Anglicorum.

W.S. fecit. 1594.

ORIENS

Felden. Lithenow.

Reicheneck. Ailtpoltstain.

Greuenberg. Altorff.

Lauff. Hershpruck.

Stirburg. Hohenstain.

Wildenfels. Hauszeck.

Botzenstain. Werd.

Pilnreut. Engeldale.

PLATE XVIII: 'Allegory of Commerce', by Jost Amman (1585)
reproduced from a revised engraving published by Wilhelm Peter Zimmermann in Augsburg (1622)
GNM, H 128.

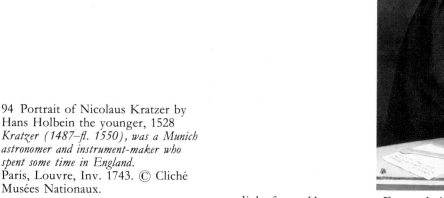

94 Portrait of Nicolaus Kratzer by
Hans Holbein the younger, 1528
*Kratzer (1487–fl. 1550), was a Munich
astronomer and instrument-maker who
spent some time in England.*
Paris, Louvre, Inv. 1743. © Cliché
Musées Nationaux.

sundials from Hartmann. From their correspondence we know that
Hartmann sent him six ivory sundials for 55° latitude, two for 54° latitude,
four small boxwood sundials for 55°, and an ivory cross sundial. Hartmann received a goblet worth 'three times as much' as the
instruments, but of course the cost of the goblet is not recorded (Zinner
I, 357–8).

Hartmann did not limit himself to the European market. One of his
designs, now in Munich, is of a diptych dial with Arabic lettering and
numerals. At the bottom of the page is the Latin inscription 'Georgius
Hartman Norembergæ fatiebat Anno obsidionis', which corresponds to
the inscription on the dial itself (fig. 96). 1529 was the year in which the
Turks besieged Vienna and were successfully defeated. This dial, and
perhaps others like it, must have been specifically aimed at the Turkish
market, the wealthy generals of the Sultan's army. The range of Nuremberg trade was obviously not adversely affected by either confessional or
political boundaries.

95 Hans Tucher, 1595
*Oval, brass fittings, with silver suspension
ring and chain. The diptych would have
been fastened at the waist by means of the
chain.*
Cat. 52.

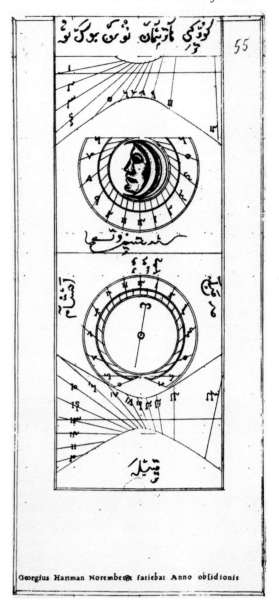

96 Engraving of inner leaves of diptych for the Turkish market by Georg Hartmann (1529)
On the top leaf (above a pin-gnomon dial for Babylonian hours) is an inscription in Arabic script which reads in translation 'Georg Hartmann of Nuremberg'. Below the south-facing equatorial dial the badly-written script seems to read 'Constantinople [latitude] 41°'. On the lower leaf the cardinal points are marked in Arabic script around the compass bowl, in which the needle is shown offset by about 10 degrees. The poor quality of the lettering suggests that it was copied by someone who did not know Arabic. The Latin inscription on the lower edge of the engraving, which means 'Georg Hartmann of Nuremberg made it in the year of the siege', possibly refers to 1529, the year in which the Turks overran Hungary and reached the gates of Vienna for the first time.
BSB, MS Rar. 434, fol. 55.

The general market: standardized instruments

Although certain instruments were obviously made for particular patrons, it is no contradication to state that the ivory diptychs were in general aimed at as wide a market as possible.   Evidence of standardization in the instruments themselves supports this view.   The similarity in size, shape and design of several groups of Paul Reinmann's instruments indicates that he produced instruments in certain basic types.   For example, three similar instruments in the exhibition of 1599, c. 1600 and 1602 are among the largest made by Reinmann (Plate IV, figs 97, 124).   Each of these has a combined lunar volvelle, wind rose and equatorial dial, with a table of about one hundred towns and their latitudes on the outside of the lower leaf.   All that varies significantly in each case is the choice of vignette and decoration around the scaphe on the inner surfaces.

Further evidence of standardization in Reinmann's output is the reproduction of the same border motifs on many different instruments.   The repeated crescent moon, star and dotted semicircle pattern (fig. 105, motif 29) is one which is found on many examples of Reinmann's work (e.g. Plate IV, figs 115, 124, 128).   A variant on this (motif 30) appears on the instrument of 1602 already mentioned (fig. 124).   Finely

97 Paul Reinmann, 1599
Cat. 43. *(Compare fig. 124).*

engraved arabesques of a similar style were also used by Reinmann and his
workshop for borders and spandrels (figs 79, 97, 120).   It seems that it
was customary to select designs for the borders, vignettes and spandrels
from existing patterns, a choice which could have been made by the maker
or by the purchasers themselves.   The more costly the instrument, the
more individual its design was likely to be.

The impression that compass-makers produced most of their instruments in a range of standard sizes is reinforced by two pieces of written
evidence.   In the first place, the statute refers to three sizes of design to
be produced by the would-be master: large, medium and small (Table
7).   From each of these, a dozen compasses were to be produced.   Secondly, a price list of instruments by Levinius Hulsius, who
traded in Nuremberg between about 1590 and 1602, included compass
sundials priced at 1, 2, 4, 6 and 10 talers (Zinner I, 392–3).   Whether these
instruments were ivory diptychs or not is unclear, but what is apparent is
that there were examples to suit all pockets – at least the pockets of a
particular cross-section of urban society.

The same blend of specialization and standardization is found in the
choice of latitudes for which the diptychs were designed.   They fall into
two main groups: those for a single latitude, and those for a range of
latitudes.   As has been suggested in the previous chapter, the latitude
found most often on the fixed instruments is approximately 48°.   Yet it
is clear that the compass-makers would produce dials for an alternative
latitude if required.   We have already seen, for example, that Duke
Albrecht of Prussia specifically asked Hartmann for two groups of compasses for 55° and 54°, appropriate for his dukedom.   An example of a
diptych for a particular latitude (51° 30′) shown here is Cat. 29.

The number and range of latitudes on the adjustable instruments are basically standardized (see Chapter six). Apart from indicating that the instrument can be used in different countries and towns, from Spain to Scandinavia, Constantinople to Cracow, nothing can be learned from most of these lists. Occasionally, however – and this only becomes evident once the standard information is recognized for what it is – there is an unusual feature which suggests that the piece was made with an individual customer in mind.

One diptych by Jacob Karner (fig. 98) has a latitude table of twenty-two towns of which many are French. This is in striking contrast to other instruments of this size made by the Karner family which usually incorporate a standard list of towns mainly from Germany and Italy. Another example of an unusual range of towns is found on an instrument from the Miller workshop (fig. 126). Of twenty-eight towns, eight have latitudes of 54° and above, including Moscow 62°, Stockholm 60° and Copenhagen 56°. The fixed gnomon is for approximately 56° latitude, which might suggest that it was made for use in northern Europe, although the equatorial dial is adjustable. Yet the list also includes more exotic locations such as 'Delphi 37°', 'Alexandria 31°' and 'Babylon 29°'.

The very design of the portable, adjustable diptych signalled its role as an object appropriate for widespread geographical distribution. While such an instrument could be used in all the towns it listed, the real function of the list was to imply that the owner was the sort of person who required such information. In the same way diaries today include maps, lists of airports, dates of holidays and religious festivals of many countries, while even wristwatches can display the current time in eight different cities across the world at the touch of a button. These can be bought by someone who never travels beyond the nearest town, but who would like to imagine doing so. Put in modern terms, the compass-makers skillfully packaged a concept of the traveller abroad for anyone with enough money to buy their instruments.

Some further literary evidence

That such Nuremberg instruments were actually used in a range of countries is, however apparent from a number of sources. Thus for example, in a council deliberation of 5 August 1578, reference is made to correspondence from the city of Strasbourg complaining that their city surveyor,

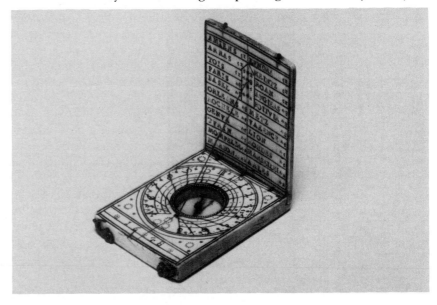

98 Jacob Karner, 1648
The number of French towns listed in the table is notable. Compare fig. 16, which has a more typical selection of places.
Cat. 49.

99 Man holding an astronomical
compendium
*Pen-and-ink drawing by the Swiss
goldsmith and painter, Urs Graf
(c. 1485–1528).*
Basel, Öffentlichen Kunstsammlung,
Kupferstichkabinett, Inv. 1978.91.

100 Title page, Peter Apian, *Folium
Populi* (Ingolstadt, 1533).
RAS.

Daniel Specklin (1536–1589), had not received compasses he had ordered directly from the Nuremberg compass-makers. The city fathers asked their compass-makers whether they had any good reason for declining to provide Specklin with instruments based on his specifications for use in his profession (Hampe, no. 349).

Correspondence between buyers and retailers within the Holy Roman Empire has already been mentioned. Examples from further afield, perhaps coincidentally from members of the same Nuremberg patrician family, provide more valuable information about the nature of supply and demand for these objects.

In January 1507 Michael Behaim wrote to his brother Wolfgang in Lisbon, a factor for a family business there. They were brothers of the better-known Martin, famed for the globe of the earth he helped to make in 1492. In his letter to Wolfgang (NStA, Behaim-Archiv 585), Michael remarked that the compasses which Erhard Etzlaub was making would be delivered in about three to four weeks when they would be sent to Lisbon. The material used for the instruments is not specified. According to Johannes Cochlaeus' *Brevis Germaniae descriptio* (1512), Etzlaub's instruments were sought after 'even in Rome' (Schnelbögl I, 12–13).

Forty years later, in 1547, Jeronimus Imhof (a member of another Nuremberg patrician family), who was living in the Italian town of Aquileja west of Trieste, wrote to Paul Behaim. One reason for writing was because he wanted to buy an ivory sundial marked for German and Italian hours from Linhart Gresel. He had seen such an instrument he admired and wanted to buy one of his own (Zinner I, 94, 326). The pattern we have already seen of personal contacts leading to the commissioning of a dial by a particular maker or retailer is again followed here.

From this written evidence, it is clear that one distinct group for which these instruments were made was that of the merchant entrepreneurs.

101 'The renewed Enfeoffment of the Imperial city of Nuremberg with the Bohemian Fiefs by Emperor Mathias, 1612'
Watercolour by Johann Theophil Prestel.
Nuremberg, Stadtmuseum Fembohaus.

This impression is reinforced by contemporary representations of people using such instruments (fig. 99). Similar images are portrayed in the illustrations found in books on instruments, aimed at the same market (fig. 100).

The fashion for amassing scientific instruments, apparatus and books in the form of special collections only became widespread in Europe during the eighteenth century. Nevertheless, it is clear that such objects already appeared in the more general *Kunstkammern* of aristocrats, and even those of Nuremberg patricians, at a much earlier date. The inventory of Philip Scherl (d. 1637), for example, contains entries which refer to a compass

102 The Astronomer
Hans Sachs and Jost Amman,
Eygentliche Beschreibung aller
Stände auff Erden *(Frankfurt, 1568).*

instrument for surveying, a compass on a staff (presumably also for surveying), and an astronomical book for one guilder (Gümbel, 333, 336). Although no instruments are recorded, the cabinet of Paul Praun (1548–1616) included the following books along with a number of similar works on measuring and mathematics: Dürer's *Underweysung der Messung* (1525), Apian's *Folium Populi* and *Instrument Buch* (1533). Praun's cabinet also contained a number of turned ivory goblets by members of the Zick family (de Murr, 490–1; see above, fig. 29).

From this variety of evidence, it can be concluded that the ivory diptychs were made in Nuremberg for both the domestic and foreign markets. These markets included wealthy urban patricians and nobles who bought the finest instruments for their own pleasure or as gifts for others. At the same time the demand for less expensive diptychs, still in ivory, was also met by the compass-makers.

This brief survey of the market has also shown that apart from their more obvious uses, such as proper time-keeping in different locations and orientation, the diptychs also had some application in the context of surveying and astronomical observation (fig. 102). In every respect, the Nuremberg compass-makers appear to have offered a service that catered for a varied clientele. It is fortunate for us that the instruments they produced, along with those from other centres, became objects of both aesthetic and technical interest to collectors of the nineteenth and early twentieth centuries (Turner, 275–9).

The sundials acquired by Lewis Evans (1853–1930), for example, form the basis of the collection in the Museum of the History of Science in Oxford (fig. 103; L. Evans). These were supplemented by those given to the Museum by J. A. Billmeir (1900–1963) in 1957. The sundials in the Whipple Museum for the History of Science in Cambridge have a similar provenance. They include the sundials donated by the founder Robert Whipple (1871–1953) and those on permanent loan from the Fitzwilliam Museum, which were originally given to the Fitzwilliam by Charles Holden-White in 1935. It is from these rich resources that the diptychs in the exhibition have been drawn.

103 Portrait of Lewis Evans
(1853–1930)
Evans is holding a diptych in his collection shown in the exhibition (Plate VI).
Painting by W. E. Miller, on loan from the Evans family.
Oxford, Museum of the History of Science. Photograph by Brian Archer.

Die elfenbeinernen Klapp-Sonnenuhren aus Nürnberg

Sonnenuhren sind für den modernen Beobachter häufig lediglich antiquierte Instrumente der Zeitmessung, die zum traditionellen Fassadenornament öffentlicher Gebäude gehören oder als Kunstobjekte ein Bestandteil formeller Gartenanlagen sind. Mit einigem Staunen wird man hier also zur Kenntnis nehmen, dass solche feststehenden Sonnenuhren keineswegs die einzigen Zeitmessungsinstrumente waren, die den wandernden Sonnenschatten zur Bestimmung der Tageszeit nutzten. Im 16 und 17. Jahrhundert wurde offensichtlich eine reiche Vielfalt von tragbaren Sonnenuhren in unterschiedlichsten Ausführungen erzeugt und diese Uhren fanden auch ausreichenden Absatz, so dass sich in manchen Städten sogar ein auf die Herstellung solcher Instrumente spezialisiertes Gewerbe entfalten konnte. Dies ist umso verwunderlicher als parallel dazu eine andere Gruppe von Handwerkern die Entwicklung der Feder-Taschenuhr vorantrieb.

Der tatsächliche Nutzen eine Sonnenuhr ist natürlich von der korrekten Ausrichtung des Schattenwerfers (gr. *gnōmōn*) abhängig. Dies ist bei einem feststehenden Instrument lediglich eine Frage der sorgfältigen Berechnung und Ausführung. Eine tragbare Uhr andererseits ist für ihren Besitzer nur dann von Vorteil, wenn sie in jeder Situation korrekt orientiert werden kann. Erste Schritte zur Überwindung dieses Problems, die um die Mitte des 15. Jahrhunderts unternommen wurden, erforderten die Zusammenarbeit von Wissenschaftler und Handwerker, danach konnten die Lösungen einfach kopiert werden; dies geschah manchmal offensichtlich ohne Verständnis für die technischen Zusammenhänge. Als wichtigste Orientierungshilfe wurde ein Kompass in die tragbaren Instrumente eingesetzt, so dass sie überall in eine Nord-Süd-Richtung gebracht werden konnten; deshalb werden Klapp-Sonnenuhren oft auch Kompass-Sonnenuhren und ihre Hersteller üblicherweise Kompassmacher genannt. Anspruchsvollere Geräte besitzen zusätzlich einen für die jeweilige geographische Breite verstellbaren Gnomon-Faden, mit dem die Auswirkungen des örtlich unterschiedlichen Einfallswinkels der Sonne korrigiert werden. Eine solche Sonnenuhr ist gewöhnlich mit einer Liste von Orten oder Ländern und ihren Breitengraden versehen.

Das vorliegende Buch bietet eine ausführliche historische Untersuchung von elfenbeinernen Diptychen, die in Nürnberg zwischen 1500 und 1700 hergestellt worden sind. Neben Nürnberg sind nur noch aus Dieppe in Frankreich eine grössere Zahl solcher Instrumente aus Elfenbein erhalten. (Dabei darf jedoch nicht übersehen werden, dass auch in anderen Orten, etwa in Augsburg, tragbare Sonnenuhren produziert wurden; diese Stücke sind aber gewöhnlich in Metall, vorzügluch in Messing, gearbeitet.) Nürnberg is von besonderem Interesse, weil hier die Verbindung zwischen wissenschaftlichem Forschen und handwerklicher Präzisionsarbeit schon im späteren 15. Jahrhundert, etwa im Wirken von Johannes Regiomontanus, zutage tritt.

Diese Studie beschränkt sich daher nicht auf eine Beschreibung und Würdigung der Instrumente selbst, sondern bemüht sich auch um eine

Aufhellung des sozialen und kulturellen Hintergrunds ihrer handwerklichen Fertigung. Die Rekonstruktion der Stuktur des Kompassmacherhandwerks macht deutlich, dass eine beschränkte Zahl von Familien das Gewerbe dominierte, nachdem es spätestens seit 1535 durch städtisches Gesetz (*Ordnung*) geregelt worden war; damit wurden die Kompassmacher strikten Regeln der Ausbildung und Qualitätsprüfung unterworfen. Für einige der Familien konnten mit Hilfe von archivalischen Quellen unter Einbeziehung bereits veröffentlicher Informationen zuverlässige Stammtafeln erstellt werden, in anderen Fällen, etwa für allgegenwärtige Familiennamen wie Miller oder Müller, sind die Eintragungen in Gerichts- und Kirchenbüchern vieldeutig und lassen keine sichere Entscheidung über Familienzusammenhänge zu.

Aus dem Handwerksstatut selbst wird klar, dass nur ein Bruchteil der Klapp-Sonnenuhren aus Nürnberg auf uns gekommen sind. Insbesondere die geringe Zahl der erhaltenen Holzdiptychen gibt zu denken, wenn man berücksichtigt, dass jeder Geselle vor seiner Zulassung zum Meisterrecht drei Dutzend Instrumente aus Birnen oder Buchsbaumholz zur Begutachtung vorlegen musste. Die Annahme liegt nahe, dass solche hölzerne Uhren die eigentlichen Gebrauchsinstrumente darstellten und abgenutzt wurden, während elfenbeinerne Diptychen als wertvoller Familienbesitz sorgfältig behandelt wurden, wenn sie nicht von vornherein schon für eine Sammlung (*Kunstkammer*) erworben worden waren. Das hochwertige Material in Verbindung mit der ansprechenden und oft sehr detaillierten Dekoration lassen vermuten, dass die Hersteller selbst bereits einen solchen spezialisierten Markt im Auge hatten.

Einige Instrumente des 17. Jahrhunderts scheinen einen solchen Trend zum Sammlerobjekt zu bestätigen. Sie sind offensichtlich kunstvoll ausgeführt, die technischen Angaben auf den Instrumenten aber sind teilweise ohne praktischen Wert; Thomas und Joseph Tucher beispielsweise kopierten gängige Epakten-Tabellen (nützlich zur Kalkulation der Datumsunterschiede zwischen Gregorianischem und Julianischem Kalender), vertauschten dabei jedoch die Zuordnungen 'Julianisch' und 'Gregorianisch' und gaben obendrein keinerlei Hinweis darauf, welches Zahlenpaar für ein bestimmtes Jahr zutreffend wäre. Obwohl sicherlich gefragt werden muss, ob der durchschnittliche Besitzer eines Diptychs jemals alle angebotenen Funktionen und Umwandlungstabellen verstand und tatsächlich nutzte, so ist in solchen Fällen die Abwesenheit astronomischer bzw. kalenderkundlicher Kenntnisse doch zu offensichtlich, um als Irrtum erklärt werden zu können. Der unmittelbare Austausch zwischen Akademikern und Handwerkern war abgebrochen, und der individuelle Hersteller wird für die Qualität seiner Instrumente allein verantwortlich; die Begutachtung durch die Gewerbevorstände war auf die Korrektheit von Ziffernblatt und Polhöhe konzentriert.

Solche Entwicklungen innerhalb des Handwerks der Kompassmacher scheinen darauf hinzudeuten, dass deutlich vor dem schliesslichen Aussterben des Gewerbes sich eine Zielverschiebung von Gebrauchsinstrument hin zum Kunstgegenstand entfaltete. Dieser Trend wird indirekt durch die Beobachtung bestätigt, dass etwa von der Mitte des 17. Jahrhunderts an die Herstellung von Klapp-Sonnenuhren mit anderen Erwerbstätigkeiten kombiniert wurde; Albrecht, Melchior und Georg Karner beispielsweise werden als Kompassmacher-Meister und als Berufsmusikanten beschrieben. Der eigentümlich stolze und zugleich gefühlvolle Rückblick auf die vergangene Bedeutung der Kompassmacher in einer Festschrift des *Rugamts* (Nürnberger Gewerbeaufsicht) von 1719 vervollständigt den Eindruck, dass letztlich die kunsthandwerklichen Gesichtspunkte in den Vordergrund getreten waren (*siehe* Table 7).

Catalogue

Forty-three Nuremberg diptychs in the exhibition are from the Museum of the History of Science, Oxford, and the remaining sixteen are from the Whipple Museum of the History of Science, Cambridge. These represent about two-thirds of the total in Oxford and just over half of those in Cambridge, which together make up a substantial proportion of the ivory diptychs extant in public collections. The horizontal compass dials (Cat. 60, Cat. 61), which are also presumed to be of Nuremberg origin, are on loan for the Cambridge venue from the Museum of London (ML).

All sundials in the Cambridge collection have recently been catalogued by David Bryden. Information on the diptychs shown here is thus based primarily on this source (Bryden). Cambridge dials are identified in the present catalogue by inventory numbers with the prefix W (Whipple). Those from the Whipple collection have three-figure numbers (e.g. W 324), while those from the Holden-White collection are represented by four figures (e.g. W 1688).

Oxford diptychs which have an inventory number prefixed by G (for Germany) were originally in the collection of Lewis Evans. They are described in Lewis Evans's original card catalogue of sundials which is kept in the Museum. Cat. 24 and Cat. 59, which have no prefix, and Cat. 58, which has no number, were also in this collection. The remaining six instruments (which have inventory numbers starting with 57–84/) were formerly in the collection of J. A. Billmeir and are described in a published catalogue and its supplement (Josten, 24–34; Maddison, 59–61).

Every instrument shown in the exhibition is represented here by at least one photograph. As these are distributed throughout the book, figure and plate numbers have been included in the catalogue entries themselves. In the index, under the maker's name, each individual instrument will have an entry.

Apart from Oxford and Cambridge, the largest public collection of Nuremberg ivory sundials in Britain is that held by the British Museum; they have been catalogued by Ward, but with few illustrations. Other collections in Europe (which have been seen by the author) include those in the Germanisches Nationalmuseum, Nuremberg, the Bayerisches Nationalmuseum, Munich, and the Museo Poldi-Pezzoli, Milan. The following publications (cited in full in the bibliography) are among the most useful sources of illustrations of Nuremberg diptychs for those who do not have access themselves to major collections: Belgian collections; Bonelli; Körber; Michel I; Milan; Rohde; Wynter & Turner.

The catalogue offers a summary rather than a comprehensive description of each instrument shown in the exhibition. In order to avoid unnecessary repetition, abbreviated phrases have been used wherever possible to indicate the standard components of each diptych. Brief explanations for these phrases are offered in the following paragraphs, and further technical details are found in Chapter one. Figures 104 and 105 illustrating makers' marks and principal decorative motifs are designed to supplement each catalogue entry.

Identification: for any instrument this may have been obtained from one or more of the following: full name, initials, date, maker's mark. In the case of unsigned or undated examples a maker's name or a provisional dating has usually been suggested, based on stylistic grounds (see Chapter six).

Materials: as nearly all the instruments are made principally of ivory and (gilt) brass, only the use of wood, bone or other metals is noted.

Colouring: the term 'colour' is used for both inorganic pigments and dyes. The sources of the five main colours (black, red, green, blue and orange/brown) which are used to fill the engraving are discussed in more detail in Chapter five.

Dimensions: the figures refer respectively to length, width, thickness (the two leaves folded together) and compass bowl diameter.

Location: W = Cambridge, G or no letter = Oxford (see above).   The inventory number is followed by references to illustrations of the instrument in this publication.

Following the system used by Bryden, the surfaces of the two leaves of a diptych are identified as follows: 1a = outer surface of upper leaf, 1b = inner surface of upper leaf, 2a = inner surface of lower leaf, 2b = outer surface of lower leaf.   In most cases the outer surfaces (1a, 2b) are described first, followed by the inner surfaces (1b, 2a).   Mottoes and instructions are transcribed in full, together with translations.   Capital letters indicate Roman capitals, lower case indicate Gothic script (black lettering).   Editorial remarks are enclosed in square brackets.

String-gnomon dials

Calibrated for common hours (two groups of twelve, from midday and midnight).   The vertical type (on 1b) usually has hour lines between 6–12–6, while the horizontal (2a) has one or more hour scales (depending on the latitude) for hours between 4–12–8 or 5–12–7.   Instruments with fixed gnomons are assumed to be for a latitude of approximately 48° unless otherwise indicated.

Pin-gnomon dials

On leaf 2a these usually indicate either Italian hours (also called Welsch, Bohemian or *horae ab occasu solis*), equal hours reckoned from sunset and numbered from about 10 to 24; Babylonian hours (also called Greek or *horae ab ortu solis*), reckoned from sunrise, numbered from about 1 to 16; or Nuremberg hours, combining the latter two systems, where daylight hours are numbered from sunrise and night hours from sunset.   The term 'scaphe' refers to a pin-gnomon dial set in a shallow hollow.

   Pin-gnomon dials on leaf 1b are usually altitude dials, indicating the sun's declination by zodiac symbol and length of day and night.   In some cases pin-gnomon dials for planetary or unequal hours (the daylight period divided into twelve equal units, varying in length according to season) are found.   These should be calibrated 1–12 (6 = noon).

Compass bowl

The compass bowl generally contains a pivot with magnetic compass needle, a glass cover and a wire ring to hold the glass in place.   These individual items are usually only referred to if they are missing or broken.   The standard markings on the bowl are also omitted from the description; these include the names of the four cardinal points, and a north-south line offset for a magnetic variation about 5°–15° east (i.e. its approximate position until the 1650s).   Motifs representing the winds and the maker's punch mark are invariably mentioned.

Wind rose

The wind rose itself may have either sixteen or thirty-two named points; in many examples there are additionally thirty-two points numbered from east through south inscribed around the compass perimeter.   The accessories of the wind rose include a brass index arm, wind vane, and compass viewing hole.   In most examples, the wind vane is missing.   It would have been kept in the small compartment with a brass cover in the side of leaf 2.

Lunar volvelle

This signifies a volvelle with a rotating brass disc for converting lunar to solar time.   The terms 'stamped' or 'engraved' indicate how the disc was manufactured (see Chapter five).   'Pierced' refers to a hole in the disc through which a representation of the moon can be seen. 'Phases of the moon indicated' means that the following words (or similar) are also inscribed: 'DER NEV MON ... DAS ERST VIERTEL ... DER VOL MON ... DAS LETZ VIERTEL' (The new moon ... the first quarter ... the full moon ... the last quarter).   These have not been transcribed.

Epact tables

The two numbers separated by a slash refer to the first numbers of the Julian and Gregorian tables respectively. These determine the year at which a particular 19-year cycle begins (when the moon and the sun assume the same relative positions in the zodiac), and the likely date(s) is included in brackets. For example, the circular epact tables on an instrument by Paul Reinmann of 1603 (Cat. 55) show Julian epacts on the outer ring, Gregorian epacts on the inner ring; these are indicated as 28/18 (beginning 1603). The full tables are as follows:

Julian: 28 9 20 1 12 23 4 15 26 7 18 29 11 22 3 14 25 6 17
Gregorian: 18 29 10 21 2 13 24 5 16 27 8 19 1 12 23 4 15 26 7

'Incorrect' epact tables are found on instruments by Thomas and Joseph Tucher. On these the terms 'Julian' and 'Gregorian' are reversed, and the epact numbers always commence 17/7.

Makers' marks

Figure 104 offers a guide to the principal marks found on most extant instruments. These are basically grouped according to family: Tucher 1–5, Troschel 6–8, Reinmann (Lesel) 9–10, Miller 11–15, Karner 17–21. Although no instruments by either Albrecht or Melchior Karner are in the exhibition, samples of their marks have been included here. Mark 18 is from London, BM, Inv. no. OA/380; mark 20 (Melchior Karner) is from Munich, BNM, Inv. no. 33/224. Mark 24 is the stamp 'N' punched by the sworn masters as a sign of quality on an instrument (see figure 57 and Chapter five). These marks are not to scale.

104 Principal makers' marks

Decorative motifs

Some of the most common motifs used to decorate the instruments are illustrated in figure 105, notably winds, moons, suns, stars and geometrical designs.   1–6 are various representations of the winds, which are usually stamped in the compass bowl.   Examples 7–9 depict the crescent moon face.   Motifs 21–24 can be used to represent either the sun or moon.   The stars 15–17 are found in varying sizes.   The motifs are not to scale.

105 Examples of decorative motifs

106 Dated 1598/9, probably by Paul Reinmann
Cat. 1.

107 Leonhart Miller, 1646
Cat. 4.

1. Dated 1598/9, probably by Paul Reinmann. Silver fittings; black and red colouring. 69 × 55 × 17 mm; 30 mm. **W 1695** (Plates XIV, XV; fig. 106).
Outer leaves engraved with two scenes from the *Apocrypha*; 1a depicting Judith holding the severed head of Holophernes, the Assyrian commander, entitled '15 IVDICH [*sic*] 99'. 2b 'SVSANNA', showing the naked Susanna in her bath resisting the advances of the two lascivious elders.
Horizontal and vertical string-gnomon dials. Large crescent moon face at top, '1598' at foot of 1b. Plain compass bowl, needle missing. Sides of leaf 2 with scrollwork foliage decoration.

2. Hans Tucher, c. 1600. Initialled, marks 2, 24. Leaf 1 gilt brass, leaf 2 ivory with wooden core. Black, red and brown colouring. 68 × 54 × 10 mm; 25 mm. **G 212** (fig. 56).
1a wind rose and hour ring; 2b lunar volvelle, stamped and pierced disc. The phases of the moon indicated, with moon motifs 7, 22; stamped 'H (mark 2) T (mark 24)'. 1b pin-gnomon dial for day length, four string attachment points for 54°–42°, inscribed 'IMPONE FILVM FORAMINI QVOD LOCI TVI POLVM INDICAT ET HORA HABEBITVR IN CIRCVLO QVI EODEM NVMERO POLARI INSCRIBITVR' (place the string in the slot which represents the latitude of your location, and the hour is to be had in the circle which is inscribed with the same latitude number). 2a string-gnomon dial with five scales; ring, glass and needle missing.

3. Thomas Tucher, before 1645. Black, red, green and orange/brown colouring. 118 × 93 × 16 mm; 36 mm. **G 214** (Plate VI).
1a wind rose; 2b lunar volvelle, engraved disc, incorrect epact tables, with phases of the moon indicated. Borders of outer leaves decorated with hook-shaped leaf motif and cast gilt brass spandrels as feet.
1b pin-gnomon dials (pins missing) for day length and planetary hours (wrongly marked 4–12–8), decorated with right- and left-facing birds. String attachment points 54°, 48°, 42°, table of twenty-one places: all those marked for 54° are incorrect even by contemporary standards, including London, Brittany, Normandy and Paris.
2a string-gnomon dial with three scales. Pin-gnomon dials for 'P 51 G' 'WELSCHE VHR' and 'P 49 G' 'NIRENPERGER VHR'.

4. Leonhart Miller, 1646. Signed, marks 12, 13. Black, red, green and blue colouring. 105 × 65 × 13 mm; 30 mm. **W 184** (fig. 107).
Borders of outer leaves decorated with foliate tendrils terminating in floral ornaments, brass bun feet. 1a wind rose, 2b lunar volvelle, stamped disc, phases of the moon with motifs 9 and 25, stamped 'L (mark 12) M'.
1b pin-gnomon dial (pin missing) for day length and common hours. Five string attachment points 54°–42°, table of twenty towns, vignette of buildings. 2a string-gnomon dial with five scales, string missing, compass bowl with mark 13 and wind motif four times, ring missing. Pin-gnomon for Italian and Babylonian hours. Inscribed 'SOLI DEO GLORIA' (glory to God alone), '1646', 'LEONHART MILLER', sun (21) moon (9) and star (15) motifs; foliate tendrils on border.

5. Hans Troschel the younger, 1618. Signed, mark 8. Red colouring. 168 × 115 × 15 mm; 40 mm. **G 248** (Plate XII; fig. 73).
Fine engraving throughout, with scrollwork of foliate tendrils terminating in floral ornaments. 1a wind rose, pin-gnomon polar dial, inscribed 'MONSTRO VIAM PERGE SECVRVS' (I show the way; go on securely) and 'TEMPVS SVMTVS EST PRECIOSISSIMVS' (time taken up is most precious). 2b lunar volvelle, engraved disc with aspectarium, table of epacts from 4/24 (beginning 1609 or 1628), planetary table and list of planetary symbols. Maker's mark 8 thrice on base, and twice in volvelle index. Decorated with figures of Sun with lion at left, Moon on crescent at right, scrollwork of leaves and flowers with cherubim. To the side is attached a hinged arm for adjusting the upper leaf as gnomon. Front clasp missing on the right.
1b pin-gnomon dials for common hours and length of day; planetary hours; Babylonian hours; Italian hours (pins for last two missing). Seven string attachment points 57°–39°. Inscription 'TEMPORE OMNIA MVTANTVR' (in time everything changes); 'NIHIL EST FVGACIVS TEMPORE' (nothing is more restless than time), table of seventy-two places. Signed 'HANNS TROSCHEL NORIBERGA FACIEBAT 1618'. 2a string-gnomon dial with seven scales, string missing. Compass with glass, ring and needle missing. Horizontal dial for common hours with upper leaf as gnomon. Pin-gnomon dial for Italian and Babylonian hours and length of day. Inscribed 'HORAE AB MERIDIE' (hours from midday); 'SOLISTICIVM HIEMALE' (winter solstice); 'SOLSTICIVM ESTIVVM' (summer solstice). Decorated with opposed winged demi-figures with foliage tails, scrollwork.

108 Maker and date unknown,
probably 17th century
Cat. 7.

6. Karner workshop? Late 17th/early 18th century; leaf 1 single ivory leaf, 2 ivory with wooden core. Black and red colouring. 50 × 34 × 11 mm; 22 mm. **W 153** (fig. 20).
1a lunar volvelle, stamped disc. 2b blank. Fixed string-gnomon dials; 1b snowflake motif (14) twice; 2a compass N–S line offset W, quatrefoil motif (11) thrice.

7. Maker and date unknown, probably 17th century; mark 23.
30 × 26 × 7mm; 9mm. **G 284** (fig. 108).
In the shape of a book, with imitation of simple geometric blind-tooling on contemporary binding. Small brass feet on outer leaves, mark 23 on 2b.
1b six-petalled flower motif (20), 2a with tiny compass (ring and glass missing), and pin-gnomon dial for Italian hours (pin missing), star motif (15) in two sizes.

8. Conrad Karner, before 1632. Signed, mark 17. Red and black colouring. 72 × 54 × 14 mm; 33 mm. **G 268** (fig. 48).
1a lunar volvelle with stamped disc, spandrels decorated with foliage; 2b blank except for faint impression of mark 17.
Fixed string-gnomon dials, string missing. 1b with eight-pointed star and reoeated motifs 12 and 13, signed 'CONRAD KARNER'; 2a compass with mark 17 twice, twisted cord holding glass. Pin-gnomon dial (pin missing) for Italian hours, decorated with motif 28.

9. Jacob Karner, 1639. Signed, dated, mark 19 (without initials). Black, red, brown and green colouring. 93 × 62 × 13 mm; 30 mm. **W 634** (fig. 16).
Outer leaves with borders of foliate tendrils scrolling from central points at upper and lower edge; 1a wind rose, index and wind vane missing; 2b lunar volvelle, disc missing, with table of epacts from 23/13 (beginning 1627); mark 19; four bun feet.
1b pin-gnomon dial for planetary hours, day and night length, decorated with star motifs (15, 17) and quatrefoils (11); four string attachment points 51°–42°, table of twenty-four towns. 2a string-gnomon dial, compass with maker's mark 19 (without initials) twice, ring a twisted cord of brass, possibly a replacement; pin-gnomon dials for Italian and Babylonian hours. Inscribed 'IACOB 1639 KARNER' and decorated with motifs 11, 15, 17 and 27.

10. Georg Karner, late 17th century, mark 21. Leaf 1 badly warped. Black and red colouring. 100 × 55 × 14 mm; 33 mm. **G 278** (fig. 50).
1a wind rose, index and wind vane missing. 2b lunar volvelle with stamped disc. Four bun feet; left front catch missing.
1b five string attachment points 54°–42°, table of twenty-four towns, decorated with repeated motifs of moon (7) and circles (13, 14). 2a string-gnomon dial with a single scale (i.e. no adjustment by latitude), string broken, compass with wind motif 2 four times and mark 21 twice. Pin-gnomon dial for Italian and Babylonian hours, with repeated motifs of the moon (7), circle (13) and sun (24).

11. Michael Lesel, c. 1629. Signed, mark 10. Black, red, green, orange/ brown colouring. 116 × 76 × 15 mm; 38 mm. **G 266** (fig. 109).
1a wind rose; outer ring marked 'SCHON DRVCK | HEITER KALT | WARM HEITTER | SCHON MIT MESIG | WARM FEICHT | RENGISCH [*sic*] | KALT FEICHT | SCHNEIG'. (fair dry, bright cold, warm bright, fair average, warm humid, rainy, cold humid, snowy). Wind as putto head blowing in each spandrel, zigzag cloud and star motif (15) along borders (cf. Cat. 39, Lienhart Miller 1627). 2b lunar volvelle with engraved and pierced disc, table of epacts from 23/13 (beginning 1627), 'EPACTA IVLIANI ANNO 1629 IST'

109 Michael Lesel, c. 1629
Cat. 11.

110 Hans Troschel, 1584
Cat. 12.

'EPACTA GREGORII ANNO 1629 IST'. Foliate tendrils rising from centre point on upper and lower borders, scrolling around a bird in each spandrel. On each outer leaf four bun feet.

1b pin-gnomon dial for Italian hours and day length (pin missing), similar dial for planetary hours and day length; below vignette of a village. Five string attachment points 54°–42°, table of forty-one towns, bottom right of table inscribed 'MICHAEL LESEL'. 2a string-gnomon dial with five scales, string missing. Compass with mark 10 twice, needle missing, crack in bowl mended by brass plate. Scaphes for Italian and Babylonian hours. Cherub heads in top spandrels, the leaf decorated with clusters of fruit and foliate tendrils.

12. Hans Troschel, 1584. Signed, dated, marks 6, 24. Black and red colouring. 105 × 62 × 13 mm; 34 mm. **G 199** (fig. 110).
1a lunar volvelle with engraved disc and associated time correction scales for hours and minutes; list of thirteen places for 51° and twelve for 54° in black lettering. 2b blank except for maker's mark 6 thrice in triangular formation, mark 24 at centre.
1b pin-gnomon dial for Italian and Babylonian hours, day and night length. Four string attachment points for 54°–45°. With instruction 'Erstlich Zih den Faden In Das Lochlein Nach deiness Landts polvs Oder Welche Am Nechsten Darbey ist' (firstly, put the string into the slotlet according to the pole of your country or which is the nearest to it), list of twenty-one places for 45° and twenty places for 48°. Inscribed 'HANS DRÖSCHELL NORMBERG FACIEBAT 1584'. 2a string-gnomon dial with four scales, compass glass cracked. Pin-gnomon dial for 49° latitude 'POLVS 49 DIES HORARVM XVI', for Italian hours, common hours and sun's declination by zodiac name.

13. Hans Troschel, late 16th/early 17th century. Signed, mark 7. Black, red and blue/grey colouring. 74 × 48 × 14 mm; 30 mm. **G 250.** (fig. 63).
1a wind-rose, inscribed 'MONSTRO VIAM PERGE SECVRVS' (I show the way; go on securely). 2b lunar volvelle with stamped disc and associated time correction

scale in hours. Inscribed 'AETAS LVNAE ET HORAE NOCTIS' (age of the moon and night hours), with motif 10 twice. At base mark 7 thrice, four bun feet.
Fixed string-gnomon dials; 1b pin-gnomon dial for Italian and Babylonian hours, base of leaf signed 'HANS TROSCHEL'. 2a compass, pin-gnomon dial for Italian and Babylonian hours, top spandrels with star motif (15) repeated.

14. Hans Troschel the younger, c. 1618. Signed, mark 8. Black and red colouring. 104 × 65 × 14 mm; 32 mm. **G 247** (fig. 111).
1a wind rose, wind vane missing. Inscribed 'MONSTRO VIAM PERGE SECVRVS' (I show the way; go on securely). 2b lunar volvelle with engraved disc and aspectarium; table of epacts from 14/4 (beginning 1618). Inscribed 'DIES AETATIS LVNAE ET HORAE NOCTIS' (day of the age of the moon and hours of the night). At base of leaf mark 8 twice; four bun feet.
1b pin-gnomon dial for common hours and day length and by zodiac symbol 'SINGNA DESCENDENTIA' and 'SINGNA ASCENDENTIA' Four string attachment points 54°–45°, table of twenty-four towns. At base of leaf 'HANNS TROSCHEL'. 2a string-gnomon dial with four scales, inscribed 'HORAE AB MERIDIE'. Pin-gnomon dial for Italian and Babylonian hours. Inscribed 'SOLSTICIVM ESTIVVM', 'HORAE AB OCCASV' and 'HORAE AB ORTU'.

15. Leonhart Miller, 1613. Signed, dated, marks 13, 14. Black, red, blue and green colouring. 92 × 56 × 12 mm; 33 mm. **G 254** (fig. 53).

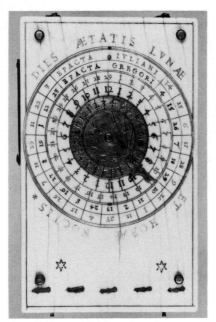

111 Hans Troschel the younger, c. 1618
Cat. 14.

Outer leaves with symmetrical design of foliate tendrils rising from centre points on upper and lower margins, bun feet. 1a wind rose, sun face at centre, index arm and wind vane missing. 2b lunar volvelle with stamped disc, mark 14 twice at base.
Fixed string-gnomon dials, string broken. 1b pin-gnomon dial for day length and by zodiac symbol; sun face at centre. 2a compass bowl with mark 13; glass, ring and needle missing. Pin-gnomon dial for Italian and Babylonian hours; base of leaf inscribed 'LIENHART MILLER 1613'. Sun motif 23 in top left spandrel, moon motif 8 top right, both with repeated stars motif 15.

16. Nicolaus Miller, 1649. Signed, initialled, dated, mark 11. Black/blue, red and brown colouring. 87 × 56 × 11 mm; 23 mm. **W 1686** (fig. 81).
Outer leaves with symmetrical design of foliate tendrils rising from centre points on upper and lower margins, small bun feet. 1a wind rose, sun face at centre, index arm and wind vane missing. 2b lunar volvelle with stamped disc. At base 'N (mark 11) M' twice.
1b pin-gnomon dial for length of day 'QVANTITAS DIEI' and by zodiac symbol 'SIGNA ZODIACI', foliate tendrils. Five string attachment points 54°–42°, table of twenty towns. 2a string-gnomon dial with five scales, inscribed 'HORÄ AB MERIDIE' (hours from mid-day) and 'SOLI DEO GLORIA' (glory to God alone). Compass bowl with mark 11, glass cracked. Pin-gnomon dial for Italian and Babylonian hours, inscribed 'NICOLAVS MILLER 1649' with sun motif 21 and repeated star motif 15.

17. Hans Tucher, 1567. Signed, dated, mark 1. Black and red colouring. 97 × 62 × 11 mm; 37 mm. **G 202** (fig. 51).
1a wind rose, combined with a universal equatorial dial, gnomon missing. Above a table of ten towns P–W, centre of leaf inscribed '1567 HANS DVCHER'. 2b table of thirty-one towns A–P. Inscribed 'WEN EIN

COMBAST RECHT SOL WEISEN RICHT IN NIT BEI EISEN' (if a compass must point correctly, do not use it near iron). At base mark 1 twice, four bun feet, each at centre of motif 18.
1b south face of equatorial dial with brass arm, fixed string-gnomon dial, pin-gnomon dial (pin missing) for 'NVRNBERGER VR', with sun face, cloud and stars. Inscribed 'DIE MIDTLER VR GEHERDT ZV DEM FADEN' ... 'DIE INDER VR GEHERDT ZV DEM LEDTERLEIN DAS AVF DER SEITEN STEDT DA 40 50 60 GRAT STEDT' (the middle dial belongs to the string ... the inner dial to the small spike which protrudes from the side where it reads 40 50 60 degree). 2a string-gnomon dial, ring and glass of compass bowl missing. Pin-gnomon dial for Italian hours, on left of leaf the scale for the equatorial dial 40°–60° by 10° to 2°.

18. Hans Tucher, 1578. Signed, dated, mark 3. Black and red colouring. 113 × 82 × 15 mm; 38 mm. **G 203** (fig. 112).
1a wind rose, wind vane missing, lunar volvelle with engraved disc which also serves as equatorial dial (gnomon missing). Inscribed around border in Gothic lower case: 'wen ich kampast recht sol weisen so richt mich nicht nahet bei eissen' (if I, compass, must point properly then do not use it near iron) 'der spöter sol nichts verachten den er kins besser machen' (the critic must not despise anything unless he could make it better). At top of leaf: 'ich kampast genandt weis den wehg dvrch alleland bei tag und nacht wen man mich bravchen mahg' (I, called compass, show the way through all countries, by day and night, if one knows how to use me). 2b list of places for 55°, 52°,48°, 45°, 42°.
1b pin-gnomon dial for Italian hours, disc as southern part of equatorial dial, vertical string-gnomon dial. Inscribed '1578' 'hans dvcher zv nvrmberg' 'wen gott wil so ist das recht zil' (if God wills, the right line is [near?]). Latitude arm on left of leaf. 2a string-gnomon dial, mark 3. Pin-gnomon dial for Italian hours and by zodiac symbol: 'die spiczen zaichen die zwölff zaichen vnd die 24 vhr tagleng' (the tips show the twelve signs [of the zodiac] and the day length out of 24 hours). Latitude scale on left side 'polvs grad' for equatorial dial 10°–70° by 10 to 2°. On right the inscription 'die raoten rislein sein die polvs grad newen auff der seiten' (the red engraved lines on the side opposite are the pole-degrees).

19. Hans Tucher, 1600. Dated, initialled, mark 2. Oval shape, leaf 2 badly cracked. Black, red and blue/grey colouring. 88 × 77 × 13 mm; 27 mm. **57–84/76** (fig. 82).
1a wind rose, two bun feet. 2b lunar volvelle with stamped and pierced disc, inscribed 'COMPASSVS PROPE FERRVM NON RECTE ASSIGNARE POTEST' (near iron the compass cannot point properly), mark 2 at top edge, two bun feet.
1b pin-gnomon dial for length of day 'QVANTITAS DIEI' and by zodiac symbol. String attachment points 54°, 48°, 42°, inscribed 'IMPONE FILVM FORAMINI QVOD LOCI TVI POLVM INDICAT ET HORA HABEBITVR IN CIRCVLO QVI EODEM NVMERO POLARI INSCRIBITVR .1.6.00.' (place the string into the slot which represents the latitude of your location, and the hour is to be had in the circle which is inscribed with the same latitude number). 2a string-gnomon dial

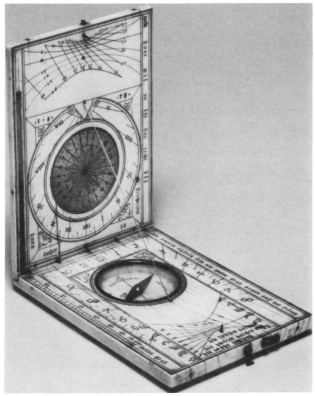

112 Hans Tucher, 1578
Cat. 18.

113 Thomas Tucher, before 1645
Cat. 20.

with three scales, compass. Pin-gnomon scaphe for Italian hours, with flower motif 19. At centre of leaf 'H (mark 2) D, 1.6.00'.

20. Thomas Tucher, before 1645. Mark 1. Black, red, green, orange/brown and blue colouring. 121 × 88 × 12 mm; 36 mm. **G 258** (fig. 113).
Outer leaves decorated with asymmetrical foliate tendrils on upper and lower margins, bun feet. 1a wind rose, wind vane missing. 2a lunar volvelle with engraved disc, incorrect table of epacts; right hand catch and suspension ring missing.
1b pin-gnomon dial for common hours, length of day and by zodiac symbol, all in triple-ringed circle cut off by edge of leaf and overlapping globe. Three string attachment points 54°–42° and 'POLVS HEG' in central triple-ringed globe marked with six lines of longitude and three lines of latitude. Table of seventeen towns. Each margin of the top half of the leaf decorated with cluster of fruit and foliate tendrils. 2a string-gnomon dial with three scales, compass with mark 1 twice. Ring missing, glass broken. Scaphes for Italian and Babylonian hours 'P 45 G', 'P 48 G', each with sun face in circle, all remaining space filled with ornament of foliate tendrils.

21. Joseph Tucher, 1642. Signed, dated, mark 5. Black, red, green, orange/red and gilt colouring. 112 × 68 × 12 mm; 27 mm. **57–84/83** (fig. 114).
On each outer leaf the four winds personified as putti heads above clouds, blowing, with foliage decoration, small bun feet. 1a wind rose with sun face at centre, on outer ring the eight winds named. 2b lunar volvelle with engraved disc and inscribed: 'driwsal angst vnd kvmer is aler menschen. plvmen' (distress, fear and

114 Joseph Tucher, 1642
Cat. 21.

sorrow are [the lot] of all men.   proverb), 'dvcher
joseph' 'nacht hvr' [*sic*].   The phases of the moon
indicated, with motifs 7 and 21 twice.
1b pin-gnomon dial for Italian and Babylonian hours,
length of day 'qvantidas diei' and by zodiac
symbol.   Decorated above with large sun face with
hook-shaped foliage at edges.   Five string attachment
points for 54°–42°, vignette of village, table of twenty
towns.   2a string-gnomon dial with five scales, compass
bowl with mark 5 twice.   Inscribed 'joseph 1642
dvcher'.   Pin-gnomon dial for Italian and Babylonian
hours, inscribed 'gros vnt klan hvr' [*sic*].   Borders and
centre of leaf decorated with hook-shaped foliage.

22.   Hieronymus Reinmann, 1559.   Signed, dated.   Red
and green colouring.   92 × 56 × 12 mm; 33 mm.   **G 198**
(fig. 52).
1a universal equatorial dial, gnomon missing, with large
sun face at centre; above a table of eighteen towns and
latitudes.   Lower spandrels decorated with motif 26.
2b blank, base of hinge inscribed 'A A'.
1b pin-gnomon dial (pin missing) for Italian and
Babylonian hours, below southern part of equatorial dial,
on right of leaf index 0–70° by 10 to 2°. Inscription
'ANNO 1558', at base of leaf 'IERONIMVS REINMAN
NORENBERGAE FACIEBAT'.   Left border decorated
with motif 26.   2a string-gnomon dial, compass bowl
with eight winds, ring, glass and needle missing.
Pin-gnomon dial for Italian and Babylonian hours,
'HORE AB ORTV ET OCCASV'.   Top corners of leaf
inscribed 'OCCASVS SEPTENTRIO ORTVS'.   On
right, arm for equatorial dial.

23.   Paul Reinmann, 1601.   Signed, dated, mark
10.   Black and red colouring. 110 × 90 × 14 mm;
31 mm.   **57–84/216** (fig. 115).
1a wind rose.   Edges inscribed 'MITTAG
NIDERGANG MITTERNACHT AVFGANG',
spandrels each with motif 21 and small star motif 15
thrice.   2b lunar volvelle with engraved disc and
associated time correction scales in hours and

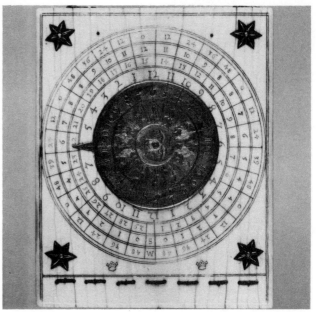

115 Paul Reinmann, 1601
Cat. 23.

minutes.   In each spandrel a six-pointed star foot cast in
gilt brass.   At base mark 10 twice.
1b string-gnomon dial; pin-gnomon dial for length of day
and by zodiac symbol; pin-gnomon dial for planetary
hours with single sun and moon motifs 8, 24, and
repeated stars motif 15; motif 19 at centre of leaf.
2a string-gnomon dial, with a series of nine concentric
circles for Italian hours 0–16 throughout the year, but
with no scale to indicate the relevant month.   Compass
bowl with N–S line W, probably a later addition.   At
base '1601' and 'PAVLVS REINMAN NORIMBERGAE
FACIEBAT'.   Bottom border decorated with motif
29.   In each spandrel wind motif 1, with repeated stars
motif 15.

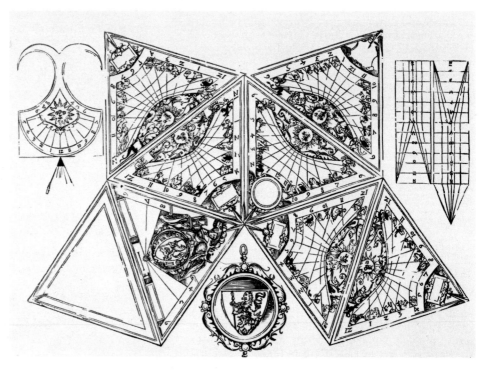

116 Print of polyhedral
dial from 16th-century
German printing block
made of limewood
(335 mm × 255 mm)
The paper print could be cut,
folded and pasted together,
thereby producing a
reasonably useful instrument.
BNM, Inv. no. F 820.

24. Georg Hartmann, 1562. Signed and dated. Red, green and brown colouring. 90 × 88 × 17 mm; 44 mm. **62–28** (Plate yy; figs 14, 72).
1a polar dial showing sun's declination by zodiac symbol. Decorated with cherub standing on grid, holding the dial at the centre of the leaf. 2b table of thirty-four towns from 37° to 54°. At front of base a compartment with brass cover for the gnomon of the polar dial.
No string-gnomon dials. Borders of inner leaves decorated with motif similar to 29. 1b south-facing equatorial dial with scale on right to elevate dial 20°–70° by 10 to 2°; inscribed 'GEORGVIS HARTMAN NORENBERGE FACIEBAT ANNO DOMINI MDLXII'; large sun face at centre, cherub head in each lower spandrel. 2a year circle divided by degrees and names of zodiac signs edged with names of winds. Compass bowl with glass and needle missing. On right brass index arm for equatorial dial.

25. Johann Gebhart, 1561. Signed, dated, mark 16. Black, red and green colouring. 93 × 56 × 13 mm; 38 mm. **G 194** (fig. 78).
1a table of eighteen towns from 54° to 39°; equatorial dial (gnomon missing) with large sun face at centre. Lower spandrels decorated with motif 27. 2b mark 16 at centre; lower edge by hinge stamped with '3' five times.
1b scale on right to elevate equatorial dial 10°–70° by 10 to 2°; pin-gnomon dial (pin missing) for Italian and Babylonian hours; fixed string-gnomon dial; southern side of equatorial dial. At centre 'ANNO 1561', at base of leaf 'IOHANN GEBHART NORENBERGE FACIEBAT'. Left border decorated with motif 26, lower spandrels with motif 27.

26. Christian Heiden, 1569. Signed and dated. Brown/black colouring. 84 × 75 × 12 mm; 46 mm. **G 200** (fig. 93).
1a three gilt brass discs. The largest near the hinge has a year circle, within this a scale of days and saint's days arranged radially about the zodiac signs; a lunar volvelle consisting of outer rotating disc and inner disc with hour index and aspectarium, pierced to show phases of the moon. The second disc shows the solar cycle from 1559 to 1587 and the third a table of epacts. 2b blank; edges of lower leaf inscribed with the four cardinal points.
1b string-gnomon dial. At top a gilt plate inscribed 'M.V.D. Thomas Loeffelholtz. patricio Norib: cons: in Septu: senatum electo. devotae gratulatio: ergo. d.d. christianus heide Anno .M. D. L. X. IX. octobris. XXVII.' (for the Master, the Right Honourable Thomas Loeffelholtz, patrician of the Nuremberg Council, the elect to the Council of the Seven Lords Elders, loyal congratulations: therefore Christian Heide gave the gift in the year 1569, on the 27th of October.) A small circular mirror is inset into the leaf, fixed by a twisted gilt brass ring. 2a string-gnomon dial; in compass bowl a gilt brass disc with orthographic projection of the sphere. Ring, glass and needle missing.

27. Hans Tucher, 1588. Signed, dated, mark 2. Black and red colouring. 112 × 90 × 13 mm; 39 mm. **G 204** (Plate VIII).
1a wind rose with the inscription 'NORT AQVILO | OST SVBSOLANVS | SVID AVSTER | WEST FAVONIVS'. Outer ring inscribed 'HIC MARINVS FAVONIVS [*sic*; misplaced] COMPASSVS SEMITAM TERRA MASRIQVE [*sic*; 's' misplaced] OSTENDIT' (this maritime compass shows the way on land as well as at sea). 2b lunar volvelle, stamped and pierced disc, with phases of the moon indicated, moon motifs 7 and 24 twice. Outer circle inscribed 'IN ORBICVLO AEQVIPARAT SE HORA NOCVRNA CVM PROXIMO NVMERO' (in the small circle the night hour comes on a level with the nearest number). At top 'COMPASSVS PROPE FERRVM NON RECTE ASSIGNARE POTEST' (near iron the compass cannot point properly). Four bun feet.
1b pin-gnomon dial for day length 'TAGLENG' and by zodiac symbol. Encircled by 'DIE SPITZ ZEIGT DES TAGS AB VND ZVNEMEN VND DIE ZWOLFF ZEICHEN' (the tip shows the increase and decrease of the day and the twelve signs). Six string attachment points 54°–39° with the instruction 'die löchlein 54 51 48 45 42 39 sein die polvs heh der land vn stett das schnürlein thv in das löchlein des lands polvs grad' (the slotlets ... are the latitudes of the countries and townships; place the string into the slotlet of the country's latitude). Below 'ILLA CVSPIS INDICAT INCREMENTVM ET DECREMETVM DIEI ET DVODECIM SIGNA' (this tip shows the increase and decrease of the day and the twelve signs), 'IMPONE FILVM FORAMINI QVOD LOCI TVI POLVM INDICAT ET HORA HABEBITVR IN CIRCVLO QVI EODEM NVMERO POLARI INSCRIBITVR M D L XXX VIII.' (place the string into the slot which represents the latitude of your location, and the hour is found in the circle which is inscribed with the same latitude number; 1588). 2a string-gnomon dial with five scales; dial for common hours using the upper leaf as gnomon. Inscribed 'ELEVATIO POLI AVFF 54 51 48 45 42 39 GRAD' and below 'HANS (mark 2) TVCHER'.

28. Hans Troschel, 1580. Dated, marks 6, 24. Black, red and green colouring. 90 × 65 × 15 mm; 25 mm. **G 240** (fig. 77).
1a lunar volvelle, engraved disc with motif 19; wind rose, wind vane missing. Inscribed 'alle die ir hofnvng stellen avf got verlest er nicht in keiner not in allen tvhn vnd lassen dein las got dein ent vnd anfang sein .HD.'. (all you who put your trust in God, He will not desert you in your distress; in all your doings and omissions, let God be your end and beginning). 2b at centre motif 19, with names of the eight winds and places where the compass may be used. Inscribed 'wen ich campast recht sol weissen so tvn mich nicht naher zu eisen. auf pollvs hog 51 gradt bin ich gemacht eben geradt 50 vnd 52 kan ich leiden | weiter sol ich meiden' (if I, compass, point properly then do not place me near to iron. I am made for pole height 51 degrees and degrees 50 and 52 may I just endure, more must I avoid). Mark 6 in lower left, mark 24 in lower right spandrel. Front left clasp missing.
1b pin-gnomon dial (pin missing) for Italian hours, day and night length. Inscribed 'dise spicz zeiget die gancz vhr sindt die roten linien' (this tip shows large hours [they] are the red lines) 'die krvmen linien mit den bloeben ziferes bedeiten des tags vndt der nach leng' (the bent lines with the blue numbers represent the length of the day and of the night'), 'tagsleng nachtleng.' (day length, night length). Three unmarked string attachment points 50°, 51° and 52°. Inscribed 'nachvolgente lender diesen campast zv bravchen', (the following [are] countries [where] this compass [might be put] to use), and a table of places. 2a string-gnomon dial for

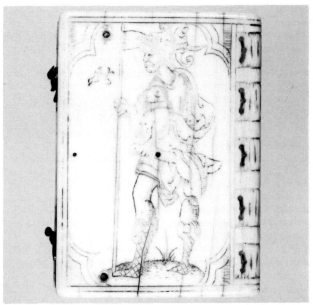

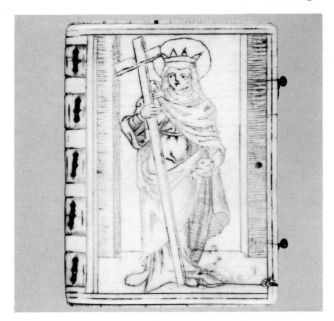

117 Hans Troschel, 1586
Cat. 29.

common hours, Italian hours, Babylonian hours and length of day.   Glass and needle missing in compass bowl.   Inscribed 'die bloeben zal ist der tagleng bedeiten die zirkel' (the blue number is the day length represent[ed by] the circles); 'krichisch tevtsch vnd welsche stvnde' (i.e. Babylonian, common and Italian hours), 'mitternacht avffgang mittag nidergang' and around border 'MORS VENIT HORA FVGIT METVAS MORTEM VENIENTEM. QVAELIBET EST INDEX FVNERIS HORA TVI.   ANNO 1580' (death comes, the hour flies, be mindful of approaching death.   Each hour is an indication of the hour of your funeral.   1500).

29.   Hans Troschel, 1586.   Dated, mark 6, in the form of a book with clasps.   Black, red and green colouring.   70 × 52 × 12 mm; 36 mm.   **G 244** (fig. 117). Engraving of St. Helena holding the true cross in her right hand on 1a.   Constantine (Helena's husband, and father of Emperor Constantine) stands on a mound, facing left on 2b.   He is bearded, with helmet and Roman-style tunic and cloak, holding a pennant in his right hand.   Mark 6 at top left.
1b pin-gnomon dial (pin missing) for Italian and Babylonian hours.   Inscribed 'SIC TRANSIT GLORIA MVNDI : AD LATITVD GRAD 51 MI 30 ANNO DOMINI M D L X X X V I' (thus the world's glory fades: for a latitude of 51° 31' in the year of the Lord 1586).   2a two string-gnomon dials, one at each edge of the leaf.   Compass bowl with ring, glass and needle missing.

30.   Late 16th/early 17th century, with mark 10 used by Paul Reinmann, in the form of a book with clasps. Black, red, blue and brown colouring.   63 × 47 × 10 mm; 30 mm.   **57–84/78** (fig. 118).
Each of the outer leaves is decorated with cast brass spandrels and clasps.   1a engraving of an unidentified bearded saint in toga, holding a spear, with a foliate tendril on either side.   2b St Peter in toga, holding a sword, with similar foliage.
Fixed string-gnomon dials.   Spandrels of each inner leaf decorated with quatrefoil motif 11 surrounded with triple-ringed quarter-circles.   Sun face at top centre of 1b, within a triple-ringed circle.   2a compass bowl with mark 10.

118 Probably Paul Reinmann, crown mark, late 16th/early 17th century
Cat. 30.

31.   Probably Conrad Karner, early 17th century, with mark 17.   In the form of a book with clasps.   Black, green, orange and brown colouring.   80 × 56 × 15 mm; 35 mm.   **G 270** (Plate XIII).
Each of the outer leaves is decorated with cast brass spandrels and clasps. 1a engraving of Virgin, arms crossed and halo, within formal border.   2b design of bordered rectangle with marked diagonals, filled with foliate tendrils of fist-shaped leaves in brown, border similar to 1a.

Fixed string-gnomon dials; 1a decorated with sun face at centre with large rays, foliate tendrils rising from lower corners on each side.   2b compass bowl, with later N–S line W, flanked by two stemmed plants with fist-shaped leaves.

32.   Maker unknown, c. 1617 (similar to Cat. 31). Silver fittings, in the form of a book with clasps. Black, green, red and brown colouring. 94 × 61 × 15 mm; 37 mm.   **W 324** (fig. 8).
Each of the outer leaves has cast spandrels and clasps.   They are similarly decorated with foliate tendrils of fist-shaped leaves rising from a centre point which terminate in a large pink at each corner.   1a wind rose, wind vane missing.   2b lunar volvelle with engraved silver disc, table of epacts 'EPACTA IVLIANI ANNO 1617' 'EPACTA GREGORI ANNO 1617' from 23/13 (beginning 1608 or 1627).
1b string-gnomon dial, silver plumb-bob suspended from top of leaf.   Decorated with sun face at centre with large rays, with foliate tendrils of fist-shaped leaves, a pink in each lower corner and a fritillary-type flower in each top corner.   2a string-gnomon dial, engraved silver disc in compass bowl with 16-point rose, N–S line W (possibly a replacement).   Decorated on each side with an urn filled with green foliage and flower.

33.   Hans Troschel, late 16th/early 17th century. Signed, in the form of a book, clasps missing.   Black, red, red/orange and green colouring. 80 × 50 × 14 mm; 13 mm.   **G 252** (Plate I).
1a blank.   2b an unidentified achievement of arms, with a shield (party per fess, in chief an eagle displayed, in base a tower within a bordure compony) and crest (a coroneted helm with mantling, surmounted by a gryphon rampant).
1b pin-gnomon dial (pin missing), showing common hours, length of day 'QUANTI = TAS DIEI' and by zodiac symbol.   Vignette of putto reclining on a mound, with hour glass in right hand and left arm resting on a skull.   In the background a running hound and trees.   At base the inscription 'HORA FUGIT MORS VENIT' (the hour flies, death approaches).   2a pin-gnomon dial for Italian and Babylonian hours, and by zodiac symbol, inscribed 'SOLSTICIVM HIEMALE' (winter solstice) 'SOLSTICIVM AESTIVVM' (summer solstice).   Small compass bowl at top centre, lacks glass, ring and needle.   Inscribed 'HANS TR = OSCHEL' at top, 'HORAE AB ORTV ET OCCASV' (hours from sunrise and sunset) at bottom.   Below dial an engraving of a pelican feeding her young from her own breast (a symbol of the Redemption).

34.   Paul Reinmann, 1578.   Signed, dated.   Black, red and brown colouring.   81 × 42 × 11 mm; 20 mm. **G 228** (figs 86, 119).
The engraving on this early example of Reinmann's work is much cruder than that of later pieces.   1a wind-rose with the eight winds, wind vane missing.   In the spandrels are engraved four men, (clockwise from top left) using a cylinder dial, a diptych dial, an armillary sphere and an astrolabe respectively, with a moon face at the top centre.   2b engraving of naked woman with Greek-style garland and veil, carrying a pot with flames (or flowers) – possibly a Vestal virgin? – framed by a decorated arch and border.
1b pin-gnomon dial for Italian hours, fixed string-gnomon dial, centre inscribed 'PAVLVS REINMAN ZV

119 Paul Reinmann, 1578
Cat. 34. *(See also fig. 86)*.

NORMBERG' with vignette of reclining putto with arm resting on a skull.   Decorated with repeated star motif 15 and 26.   2a string-gnomon dial, compass bowl with glass, ring and needle missing.   Pin-gnomon dial for Babylonian hours.   Decorated with geometric border and star motifs 15, 16.

35.   1611, probably Reinmann workshop, mark 10. Black, red and brown colouring.   95 × 70 × 13 mm; 33 mm.   **W 1689** (fig. 120).
1a wind rose, wind vane missing.   2b lunar volvelle with stamped disc, table of epacts 'EPACTA IVLIANI ANNO 1611' 'EPACTA GREGORII ANNO 1611' from 23/13 (beginning 1608 or 1627).   Mark 10 at top centre.   Bun feet, leaf damaged with brown-green stain. 1b pin-gnomon dial for length of day and by zodiac symbol, another for planetary hours, decorated with stars motif 15.   Five string attachment points 54°–42°, list of thirty-two towns.   2a string-gnomon dial with five scales.   Compass bowl blank, needle replaced. Pin-gnomon dial for Babylonian hours with snowflake motif 14 twice, another for Italian hours with quatrefoil motif 11 twice.   Between these a vignette of putto/androgyne reclining on mound below tree, head leaning on right hand with elbow resting on a skull and left arm holding hour glass on knees.   Spandrels decorated with arabesque foliage.

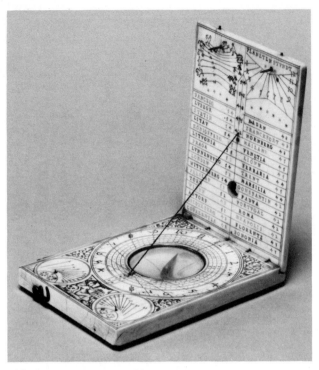

120 Crown mark, probably
Reinmann workshop, 1611
Cat. 35.

incorrect table of epacts, with phases of the moon
indicated. 2b volvelle with stamped brass disc with hour
index 1–12, 1–12, outer scale marked 8–24, for converting
between common hours and Babylonian or Italian
hours.   Bun feet.
1b pin-gnomon dial (pin missing) for day length
'QVANTIDAS DIEI' and by zodiac symbol.   Another
(pin missing) for Italian hours 'WELSCH VHR'.
Fixed string-gnomon dial, at centre sun face within a
circle.   Overlaps a lower circle with vignette of a
woman/androgyne reclining on a mound, leaning on right
hand with elbow resting on a skull and bones and left
arm holding hour glass on knees.   Decorated with
foliage of hook-shaped leaves.   2a string-gnomon dial,
with inset silver hour ring, combined with a wind
rose.   Compass bowl with mark 1 twice, glass and needle
missing.   Pin-gnomon dials for Italian hours 'WELSCH
VHR' and Babylonian hours 'GROS VHR'.   Decorative
foliage of hook-shaped leaves around the base of the
central dial.

38.   Leonhart Miller, 1613.   Signed, dated, marks 13,
14.   Black, red, green and brown colouring.
104 × 71 × 13 mm; 32 mm.   **W 1685** (fig. 121).
1a wind rose, sun face at centre, index arm and wind
vane missing.   Eight wind characteristics 'SCHON
DRVCKEN | HEITER KALT | WARM HEITER |
SCHON MITELMESIG | WARM FEICHT |
RENGISCH [*sic*] | KALT FEICHT | SCNNEIG' (fair
dry, bright cold, warm bright, fair average, warm humid,
rainy, cold humid, snowy).   Later series of letters

36.   Thomas Tucher, before 1645.   Mark 1.   Black, red,
blue, orange/brown, green and gilt colouring.   125 × 77
× 16 mm; 37 mm.   **G 223** (Plate VII; fig. 83).
The outer surface of each leaf has fine cast spandrels and
clasps.   The upper and lower margins are each decorated
with a central cluster of fruit and leaves, with foliate
tendrils terminating in floral ornaments (cf. Cat. 41).
1a wind rose, with wind names and wind motif 5 four
times.   2b lunar volvelle with stamped disc, incorrect
table of epacts.
1b pin-gnomon dial for length of day and by zodiac
symbol 'QUANTIDASS [*sic*] DIEI', within triple-ringed
circle cut off by edge of leaf and overlapping
globe.   Five string attachment points, three originally
marked for 54°, 48°, 42°, the other two (added later?) for
c. 50° and 45°, within a central triple-ringed globe
marked with six lines of longitude, and three of
latitude.   At base a vignette of naked androgyne/woman
reclining on a green mound with foliage, with right arm
resting on a skull/mask, left arm holding hour glass on
knee.   Within a triple-ringed semi-circle with arcs of
three smaller circles above.   Borders decorated with
foliate tendrils of hook-shaped leaves terminating in fruit
and floral ornaments.   2a has similar decoration.
String-gnomon dial (string missing) with three scales,
compass bowl with mark 1 twice.   Glass, ring and needle
missing.   Below scaphe for 'P 50 G' 'POLNISCHE
VHR' (time reckoning equivalent to Italian hours), with
T (mark 1) D.

37.   Thomas Tucher, before 1645.   Mark 1.   Gilt brass
and silver fittings.   Black, red, green and blue colouring.
120 × 80 × 15 mm; 33 mm.   **W 1680** (fig. 87).
The outer leaves both have wide border decorations of
bound wreaths.   In each spandrel is a cherub head.
1a lunar volvelle with engraved and pierced disc,

121 Leonhart Miller, 1613
Justice reclining on a mound.
Cat. 38. *(See also Plate III).*

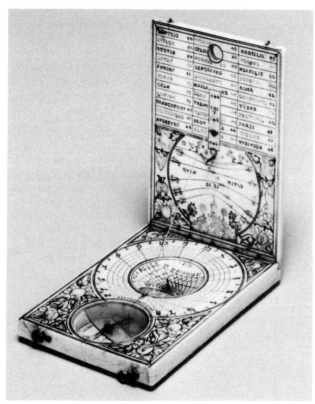

122 Leonhart Miller, 1627
Cat. 39.

scratched between points. Top and bottom margins of
leaf decorated with foliate tendrils with fruit and flower
ornaments, bun feet. 2b quadrant, lacking
plumb-bob. Below a vingette of Justice reclining on a
mound, sword in left hand, balance in right hand, with
running dog, trees and flowers. Mark 14 twice at base,
bun feet.
1b pin-gnomon dial (pin missing) for day length
'QVANTITAS DIEI' and by zodiac symbol. Top
margins decorated with symmetrical design of foliate
tendrils rising from centre points. Six string attachment
points 54°–39°, table of thirty towns. 2a string-gnomon
dial (string missing) with six scales, compass bowl with
mark 13. Below a scaphe for Italian and Babylonian
hours, decorated with sun face and inscribed
'LIENHART MILLER 1613'. Borders of leaf with
similar decoration as on 1b.

39. Leonhart Miller, 1627. Signed, dated, initialled,
mark 12. Black, red, green, orange/red, blue and gilt
colouring. 100 × 75 × 13 mm; 34 mm. **G 256** (fig.
122).
1a wind-rose, sun face at centre, wind vane missing.
Wind as putto head blowing in each spandrel, zigzag
cloud and star motif 15 along borders (cf. Cat. 11,
Michael Lesel). 2b lunar volvelle, disc missing, with
phases of the moon indicated, moon motifs 8 and 21
twice. At base 'L (mark 12) M' twice. On each leaf
four bun feet.
1b table of thirty-three towns, five string attachment
points 54°–42°, pin-gnomon dial for day length
'QUANTITAS DIEI' and by zodiac symbol. Vignette of
village with trees, lower margins decorated with clusters
of fruit (grapes, pomegranates, etc.) and leaves. Similar
decoration on 2a. String-gnomon dial with five scales,

inscribed 'SOLI DEO GLORIA' (glory to God
alone). At centre a scaphe for Italian and Babylonian
hours, with sun face and inscribed 'LIENHART
MILLER 1627'. Below compass bowl with wind motif
6 four times. Glass cracked, ring and needle missing.

40. Joseph Tucher, before 1644. Mark 5. Black, red,
orange/brown and green colouring. 126 × 79 × 13 mm;
34 mm. **57–84/82** (Plate IX).
The outer leaves are each decorated with the four winds
personified as putti-like heads above clouds, blowing,
with hook-shaped leaves; bun feet (cf. Cat. 53 by same
maker). 1a wind rose with sun face at centre, wind vane
missing. 2b lunar volvelle, stamped disc, table of
incorrect epacts, with phases of the moon, moon motifs 7
and 21 twice.
1b pin-gnomon dial (pin missing) for Italian hours,
Babylonian hours, day and night length and by zodiac
symbol. Large sun face at top centre, vignette of two
leaping dogs facing each other, with hook-shaped
foliage. String attachment points 54°, 48°, 42°, table of
eighteen towns. 2a string-gnomon dial, compass bowl
with mark 5 twice, wind motif 3 four times. Two
identical scaphes for Italian hours, each with sun face.

41. Thomas Tucher, before 1645. Mark 1. Black, red,
orange/brown, green, blue colouring. 140 × 77 ×
15 mm; 37 mm. **G 269** (Plate V).
1a wind rose. Engraved with two Ottoman Turks, each
standing on a mound; the one on left facing right with
spear and plumed hat, scimitar, moustachioed; the one on
right facing left with hat derived from fruit emblem
(pomegranate), staff and scimitar. Hook-shaped leaf
foliage. Similar decoration on 2b: left-hand figure with
hammer and scimitar, right-hand figure with staff and
scimitar. Lunar volvelle with stamped disc.
1b on left pin-gnomon dial for day length and by zodiac
symbol, within double-ringed circle; similar dial on right
for Italian hours. At centre string attachment points 54°,
48°, 42° within small triple-ringed globe marked with six
lines of longitude and two of latitude. Connected to
three triple-ringed circular arcs at base of leaf by a series
of radial lines. 2a string-gnomon dial with three scales,
compass bowl with mark 1, glass and needle
missing. On left scaphe for 'P 51 G' 'PENMISCHE
VHR' (time reckoning equivalent to Italian hours),
similar on right 'P 45 G' 'WELSCH VHR'. Each leaf is
decorated with two large clusters of fruit and leaves (cf.
Cat. 36).

42. Paul Reinmann, c. 1600. Signed, marks 10,
24. Black, red, green, orange/brown, blue and gilt
colouring. 142 × 95 × 16 mm; 48 mm. **57–84/215**
(Plate IV).
1a gilt brass volvelle with wind rose; combined with
lunar volvelle, universal equatorial dial, zodiac and
calendar scale. Inscribed 'TEMPORA LABVNTVR
TACITISQVE SENESCIMVS ANNIS | ET FVGIVNT
FRENO NON REMORANTE DIES' (the times slip
away and we grow old with the silently passing years;
there is no bridle that can curb the flying days: Ovid,
Fasti Bk 6, lines 771–2), and 'wen ich kumpast recht sol
weissen so richt mich nicht nahe bey eissen' (if I,
compass, must point properly then do not use [direct] me
nearby iron). Borders decorated with motif 29.
2b table of one hundred places, at base mark 10 twice,
with faint mark 24.
1b pin-gnomon dial for planetary hours, day and night

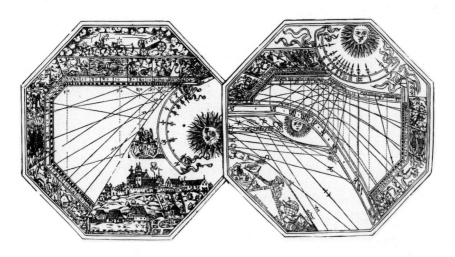

123 Engraving of two octagonal
dial faces
*This richly ornamented design, signed
'F.S.W.', is found in a collection of
Georg Hartmann engravings.*
BSB, MS Rar. 434, fol. 38.

length, and by zodiac symbol. Top part of leaf
decorated with foliate tendrils with flowers and
snails. Below string-gnomon dial, gilt brass disc as
south side of equatorial dial. At base 'PAVLVS
REINMANN NORIMBERGAE FACIEBAT'.
2a string-gnomon dial, compass bowl with later N–S line
W. Below a scaphe for Italian and Babylonian hours,
decorated with motif 19. Top spandrels decorated with
arabesques, on each side of scaphe an ornate two-handled
urn filled with sprays of flowers and leaves. Borders of
both leaves decorated with motif 29.

43. Paul Reinmann, 1599. Signed, dated, mark 10.
Black and red colouring. 153 × 94 × 19 mm; 48 mm.
G 230 (fig. 97).
1a wind rose, combined with lunar volvelle, engraved
disc with window to view lunar date and time correction;
may also be used as an equatorial dial (gnomon
missing). Table of twenty-six towns. Spandrels
decorated with arabesques. 2b table of one hundred
towns. On one edge of leaf 2 a table of epacts, on the
other a brass scale for the equatorial dial.
1b pin-gnomon dial for planetary hours, day and night
length and by zodiac symbol. Vignette of putto
reclining on a mound, left elbow resting on a mask/skull
next to a flower, with hour glass and view of village in
the background. Above a central sun face and
clouds. String-gnomon dial for about 50°, gilt brass disc
as south side of equatorial dial. At base 'PAVLVS
REINMAN NORIMBERGAE FACI'. 2a string-
gnomon dial, compass bowl with mark 10 twice, glass
cracked. Dated '1599'. Below a scaphe for Italian and
Babylonian hours, with large sun face. Bowl flanked on
each side by a Roman soldier carrying a pennant; top
spandrels engraved with cherub heads (cf. Cat. 44).
Borders of each leaf finely decorated with arabesques of
leaves, flowers and birds.

44. Paul Reinmann, 1602. Signed, dated, mark 10.
Black and red colouring. 138 × 88 × 17; 46 mm.
W 1687 (fig. 124).
1a wind rose combined with lunar volvelle, engraved disc
with window to view lunar date and time correction; may
also be used as an equatorial dial (gnomon
missing). List of twenty-eight towns. On side of leaf a
latitude arm. 2b list of one hundred towns, at base mark
10 twice.

1b pin-gnomon dial for planetary hours, day and night
length and by zodiac symbol. Vignette of amorous
couple, lutenist and violist in contemporary dress, central
sun face and clouds above. String-gnomon dial, gilt
brass disc as south side of equatorial dial. At base the
inscription 'PAVLVS REINMAN NORIMBERGAE
FACIEB'. Borders decorated with motif 30. 2a string-
gnomon dial, compass with mark 10 twice. Below a
scaphe for Italian and Babylonian hours, with sun face.
Bowl flanked on each side by a naked warrior carrying a
pennant and shield; top spandrels engraved with blowing
winds (cf. Cat. 43). Borders decorated with motif 29.

124 Paul Reinmann, 1602
Cat. 44. *(Compare fig. 97).*

45. 1611, probably by Reinmann workshop, mark 10. Black and red colouring. 140 × 100 × 15 mm; 54 mm. **G 238** (fig. 62).
1a wind rose, wind vane missing. Outer ring marked 'SCHÖN DRVCKEN | HEITER KALT | VVARM HEITER | SCHÖN MITELMESIG | VVARM FEICHT | RENGISCH [*sic*] | KALT FEICHT | SCHNEIG' (fair dry, bright cold, warm bright, fair average, warm humid, rainy, cold humid, snowy). 2b lunar volvelle, disc missing, with associated time correction scales in hours (S) and minutes (M), disc missing, and table of epacts 'EPACTA IVLIANI ANNO 1612 IST...' 'EPACTA GREGORII ANNO 1612 IST...' dated from 1612 to 1630, but beginning 23/13 (i.e. from 1608 or 1627). Outer ring decorated with scrollwork foliage. Each leaf has four finely cast pierced spandrels.
1b on left a pin-gnomon dial for day length with vignette of village, similar dial on right for planetary hours with vignette of mountain villages, lake and boat. Six string attachment points 54°–39°, table of fifty-four towns. Bottom border decorated with repeated motif 26. 2a string-gnomon dial with six scales, mark 10 punched twice at base of hour ring. Compass bowl with wind motif 2 four times; glass, ring and needle missing. Below, two scaphes for Italian and Babylonian hours, each decorated with sun face. Between scaphes an engraving of the Woman of the Apocalypse, standing on a crescent moon (*Revelation* 12.1). Side borders of leaf decorated with roses (symbol of the Virgin), pinks and foliage; top spandrels with cherub heads.

46. Karner workshop? Late 17th/early 18th century. Mark 22. Leaf 1 single ivory leaf, 2 ivory with wooden core. Black and red colouring. 49 × 38 × 13 mm; 20 mm. **W 1694** (fig. 74).
1a lunar volvelle, disc missing. 2b mark 22.
1b half sun at top; 2a compass N-S line W, snowflake motif 14 twice. Fixed string-gnomon.

47. Conrad Karner, 1623. Signed, mark 17. Black, red, green, orange/brown colouring. 113 × 78 × 15 mm; 38 mm. **W̄ 1682** (fig. 125).

125 Conrad Karner, 1623
Cat. 47.

1a wind rose; split in leaf repaired by two brass plates. 2b lunar volvelle with stamped disc, table of epacts 'EPACTA IVLIANI ANNO 1623' 'EPACTA GREGORI ANNO' from 12/13 (beginning 1608 or 1627). Upper and lower margins of each leaf decorated with foliate tendrils from centre point scrolling to left and right with first-shaped leaves; bun feet.
1b pin-gnomon dial for planetary hours 'DIE PLANETEN STVND', length of day 'DIE TAG LENG' and night and by zodiac symbol. Five string attachment points 54°–42°, table of twenty towns. Vignette with foliate tendrils, top margins with repeated step motif. 2a string-gnomon dial with five scales, compass bowl with mark 17 twice. Below pin-gnomon dial for Italian and Babylonian hours, beneath 'CONRAD KARNER' and star motifs 15 and 17 twice. Borders with foliate tendrils of fist-shaped leaves.

48. 1664, mark 14 of Miller workshop. Black, red and blue colouring. 127 × 75 × 16 mm; 50 mm. **57–84/218** (fig. 126).
1a wind rose with the eight winds; below a universal equatorial dial (gnomon missing) 'HOROLOGIV[M] GENERALE' (general time-piece). Inscription around the wind rose 'MONSTRO VIAM PERGE SECVRVS' (I show the way; go on securely). Spandrels decorated with star motifs 15. 2b lunar volvelle, with stamped disc, table of epacts from 1/21 (beginning 1663) 'EPACTA IVLIIANA AN 63' 'EPACTA GREGORI 63'. Table of twenty-eight towns, including eight of 54° or above. At base mark 14 twice. Each leaf has bun feet. The hinged arm and latitude-scale for the equatorial dial are riveted to the sides of 1 and 2 respectively.
1b pin-gnomon dial for planetary hours, length of day and by zodiac symbol 'SIGNA ZODIACI ET QVANTITAS DIE'. A planetary table 'HORAE ET TABVLA PLANETARVM'. Below southern part of equatorial dial 'HOROLIGIV[M] GENERALE' [most 'E's are punched reversed as mirror images]. 2a string-gnomon dial for about 56° latitude, compass divided 10°–180° × 2 by 10 to 5°. Below a scaphe for Italian and Babylonian hours 'HORAE AB ORTV ET OCCASV SOLIS', '1664' at top edge of scaphe. Top left spandrel with moon motif 9, right with sun motif 21, both with stars motif 15.

49. Jacob Karner, 1648. Dated, mark 19. Black and red colouring. 63 × 48 × 11 mm; 20 mm. **W 950** (fig. 98).
1a blank, 2b also blank except for mark 19, and white underside of replacement compass bowl.
1b Table of twenty-two towns, mainly French; four string attachment points 51°–42°. 2a string-gnomon dial with four scales, compass bowl a replacement. At base '1648'; decorated with motifs 13, 14, 15.

50. Hans Tucher, late 16th/ early 17th century. Initialled, marks 2, 24. Black and red colouring. With wooden case covered with tooled leather. 100 × 78 × 12 mm; 34 mm. **G 210** (fig. 57).
1a wind-rose; inscribed 'HIC MARINVS COMPASSVS SEMITAM TERRA MARIQVE OSTENDIT' (this maritime compass shows the path on land as well as at sea). 2b lunar volvelle, with stamped and pierced disc, with phases of the moon indicated. Inscribed 'COMPASSVS PROPE FERRVM NON RECTE

ASSIGNARE POTEST' (near iron the compass cannot
point properly).   At bottom right mark 24 and 'H (mark
2) D'.   Additional decoration of fleur-de-lys and flower
motifs repeated on border.   Left front clasp missing,
right front clasp incomplete.
1b pin-gnomon dial for length of day and by zodiac
symbol.   Inscribed 'IMPONE FILVM FORAMINI
QVOD LOCI TVI POLVM IN = DICAT ET HORA
HABEBI = TVR IN CIRCVLO QVI EODEM
NVMERO POLARI INSCRIBITVR' (place the string in
the slot which represents the latitude of your location,
and the hour is found in the circle which is inscribed
with the same latitude number) 'ILLA CVSPIS
INDICAT INCREMENTVM ET DECREMENTVM
DIEI ET DVODECIM SIGNA' (that tip shows the
increase and decrease of day length and the twelve signs
[of the zodiac]), seven string attachment points 57°–39°.
2a string-gnomon dial (string broken) with six scales, one
of these on the rectangular border, 'POLVS GRADVS'.
Compass bowl with brass wind-rose, glass, ring and
needle missing.   Scaphe for Italian hours inscribed
'CABRICORNVS' 'CANCER'.   Bowl decorated with
motif 19, 'MAIVS HORO = LOGIVM' (the large
clock).

51.   Paul Reinmann, 1608.   Signed, initialled, mark
10.   Black and red colouring.   111 × 91 × 15 mm;
30 mm.   With an 18th-century box covered in
unpolished shagreen and lined with red velvet.   **W 1688**
(fig. 79).
1a wind rose, edges marked with cardinal points
'SEPTENTRIO OCCASVS MERIDIES ORTVS'.
2b lunar volvelle, stamped disc, with associated time
correction scales in hours and minutes, table of epacts
1608 by year to 1626, 'EPACTA IVLIANI ANNO 1608
IST' 'EPACTA GREGORII ANNO 1608 IST',
beginning 23/13 (beginning 1608).   Four bun feet.   The
spandrels of each leaf decorated with arabesque foliage.

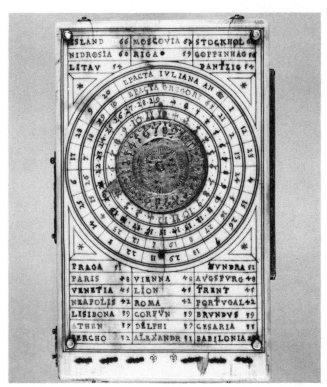

126 1664, with fleur-de-lys of Miller
workshop
Cat. 48.

127 Charta Cosmographica
Peter Apian, Cosmographia *(Antwerp, 1553)*.
RAS.

1b pin-gnomon dial for day length and by zodiac symbol, another for planetary hours, 'PLANETEN STVND'. Table of forty-five towns, six string attachment points for 54°–39°. 2a string-gnomon dial with six scales. At centre a scaphe for Italian and Babylonian hours, sun face in circle. Below compass bowl with ring missing. Spandrels decorated with arabesques of leaves and flowers. Below inscribed 'SOLI DEO GLORIA' (glory to God alone) 'PAVLVS REINMAN NORIMBERGAE FACIEBAT' with mark 10 and initials 'PR' above.

52. Hans Tucher, 1595. Oval, brass fittings, with silver suspension ring and chain. Dated, initialled, marks 2 and 24. Black and red colouring. 108 × 80 × 16 mm; 37 mm. **G 206** (fig. 95).
1a wind rose, with eight winds, inner ring reading 'schönm | kalt schön | schön | hell schön | ge wilkig | regen | trieb | schne schön' (fair, cold fair, fair, bright fair, cloudy, rain, overcast, snow fair). Inscribed 'HIC MARINVS COMPASSVS SEMITAM TERRA MARIQVE OSTENDIT' (this maritime compass shows the path on land as well as at sea), border inscribed 'DER SPÖDTER SOL NICHTS VERACHT EN DEN ER KANS BESSER MACHTEN' (the critic should despise nothing unless he can make it better). 2b lunar volvelle with stamped and pierced disc, with phases of the moon indicated, moon motifs 7 and 24 twice.
Inscribed 'NACHT CAMPAST'. Near top 'H (mark 2) D', below it mark 24. The names of the cardinal points are engraved around the edge of leaf 2.
1b pin-gnomon dial for length of day and by zodiac symbol. Seven string attachment points 57°–39°. Instruction 'die löchlein sein die polvs heh der land vnd stett | das schnürlein thv in das löchlein der land vnd stett' (the slotlets are the latitudes of the countries and townships; place the string into the slotlet of the countries and townships); below instruction 'IMPONE FILVM FORAMINI QVOD LOCI TVI POLVM INDICAT ET HORA HABEBITVR IN CIRCVLO QVI EODEM NVMERO POLARI INSCRIBITVR' (place the string into the slot which represents the latitude of your location, and the hour is found in the circle which is inscribed with the same latitude number). Border inscribed 'COMPASSVS PROPE FERRVM NON RECTE ASSIGNARE POTEST' (near iron the compass cannot point properly). 2a string-gnomon dial with seven scales, compass bowl with ring missing. 'ELEVATIO POLI' at base; '1595' in tiny figures near hinge.

53. Joseph Tucher, before 1644. Mark 5. Black, red, orange/brown and green colouring. 111 × 69 × 12 mm; 36 mm. **W 1696** (fig. 80).
The outer leaves are each decorated with the four winds personified as putti-like heads above clouds, blowing, with hook-shaped leaves; bun feet. 1a wind rose with sun face at centre, wind vane missing. 2b lunar volvelle, stamped disc, incorrect table of epacts.
1b pin-gnomon dial (pin missing) for Italian hours, Babylonian hours, day and night length and by zodiac symbol. Decorated above with hook-shaped leaf motif, below vignette of village. String attachment points 54°, 48°, 42°, table of eighteen towns. 2a string-gnomon dial, compass with mark 5 twice, wind motif 3 four times, ring missing. Below a scaphe for Italian hours with sun face. Borders decorated with foliate tendrils of hook-shaped leaves.

54. Johann Gebhart, 1556, Signed, dated, mark 16. Red, green/black? colouring. 93 × 54 × 12 mm; 36 mm. **W 1681** (fig. 46).
1a table of twenty towns 54°–39°. Below an equatorial dial (lacks gnomon), decorated with repeated star motif 15 and zigzag lines. 2b blank except for mark 16 at centre.
1b pin-gnomon dial for Italian hours, string-gnomon dial, southern side of equatorial dial, scale of latitudes on right. At top the date 1556, at base of leaf 'IOHANN GEBHART'. Left hand border decorated with geometric motif. 2a string-gnomon dial, compass bowl with eight winds, ring replaced by red and white twisted cord. Pin-gnomon dial for Italian and Babylonian hours, 'AD SXTVM [*sic*] CLIMA HOROLOGIM [*sic*] INTEGRVM' (a sound time-piece for the sixth region [of the earth]). Inset brass index arm for equatorial dial. Around the top edge of the leaf 'OCCASV[S] SEPTENTRIO ORTVS'.

55. Paul Reinmann, 1603. Signed, dated, marks 10 and 24. Black, red and brown colouring. 98 × 55 × 14 mm; 30 mm. **G 234** (fig. 128).
1a wind rose, wind vane missing. Combined with lunar volvelle, engraved disc with window to view lunar date and time correction; may also be used as an equatorial dial. Epact tables from 28/18 (beginning 1603). Top border decorated with motif 29. 2b table of forty towns 62°–37°, at base mark 10 twice and mark 24.
1b pin-gnomon dial for day length and by zodiac symbol, string-gnomon dial. Gilt brass disc as southern side of

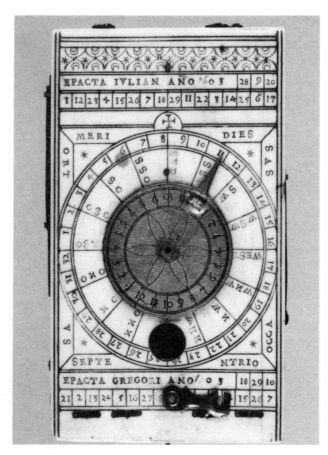

128 Paul Reinmann, 1603
Cat. 55.

129 Thomas Tucher, before 1645
Cat. 56.

equatorial dial, brass latitude arm.   In centre '1603', at base 'PAVLVS REINMAN FACIEBAT'.   2a string-gnomon dial.   Below a scaphe for Italian and Babylonian hours with motif 18.   In each top spandrel wind motif 1, lower borders decorated with motif 29.

56.   Thomas Tucher, before 1645.   Mark 1.
Three-leaved compendium with brass plate.   Black, red, green and orange colouring.   112 × 88 × 22 mm; 37 mm.   **G 217** (fig. 129).
1a wind rose.   Small foliate tendrils of hook-shaped leafs rising from central points on top and bottom margins. Bun feet.   1b pin gnomon dial (pin missing) for planetary hours (incorrectly marked), day length and by zodiac symbol, 'QVANTIDAS [*sic*] DIEI'.   String

attachment points 54°, 48°, 42° (marked), further points at c. 51°, 56°.   These holes may have been added later.   Table of fifteen towns.   Some of the latitudes have been altered: PRAWANT 42 to 51, SWETEN 54 to 57, DENEMARG 54 to 56, LIFLANT 54 to 57. Middle of leaf decorated with foliate tendrils of hook-shaped leaves scrolling to left and right.
2a string-gnomon dial (string missing) with three scales, compass bowl with mark 1 twice, glass cracked.   Below a pin-gnomon dial 'P 45 G' 'GROS VNT KLAN VR' for Italian and Babylonian hours, hours of the night 'TIE NACHT LENG' and day 'DIE TAG LENG'.   Foliate tendrils of hook-shaped leaves decorating borders.
2b volvelle for interconverting common and Italian hours.   On the ivory leaf 'VERGLEIGVNG GROS

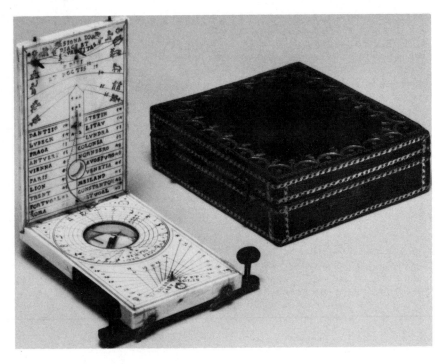

130 1674, with fleur-de-lys mark of
Miller workshop
Cat. 57.

VNT KLEIN VHR' (comparison of large and small hours) with common hours 4–12–8 and scale for length of day 'TAG LENG'. The brass disc engraved 'DAS IST DIE KROS VHR' with hour ring 8–24. Leaf decorated with left- and right- facing birds, foliate tendrils of hook-shaped leafs rising from central points on bottom border.
3a shallow rectangular space with hinged gilt brass semicircular support carrying equatorial dial with hinged graduated quadrant.
3b ivory covered; gilt brass plate with year circle showing signs of the zodiac, degrees and hour index. At the centre a lunar volvelle and aspectarium, pierced to show phases of the moon. Outside this another rotating band with lunar day calendar showing daily differences in the moon's age in minutes and hours. Two of the four small bun feet are missing.

57. Miller workshop, 1674. Mark 15. Black, red and blue colouring. 92 × 57 × 13 mm; 24 mm. With wooden box covered with tooled leather, possibly 18th century. **G 262** (Fig. 130).
1a wind rose, inscribed 'MONSTRO VIAM PERGE SECVRVS' (I show the way, go on securely). 2b lunar volvelle with stamped disc. Inscribed 'AETATIS LVNAE ET HORAE NOCTIS' (of the age of the moon and the hours of the night). At base mark 15. To the original instrument a brass strip with two feet adjusted by screws and another small turned foot have been added, as well as a plumb-line and bob kept in the compartment originally intended for the wind-vane, now missing. These modifications, together with the wooden box, are thought to have been 18th-century additions.
1b pin-gnomon dial for length of day and by zodiac symbol, inscribed 'SIGNA ZODIACI ET QVANTITAS DIEI ET NOCTIS'. Extra pin at top left-hand corner of leaf. Five string attachment points 54°–42°, table of twenty towns. 2a string-gnomon dial with five scales, inscribed 'SOLI DEO GLORIA' (glory to God alone). Compass bowl with brass pointer for 15° W. Below a pin-gnomon dial for Italian and Babylonian hours, 'HORAE AB ORTV ET OCCASV SOLIS'. '1674'. Top left spandrel with motifs 13, 15, right spandrel with motif 9, 15.

58. Karner workshop? Late 17th/early 18th century. Leaf 1 single bone leaf, 2 bone with wooden core. Black and green colouring. 45 × 30 × 8 mm; 19 mm. Oxford, Lewis Evans collection, **no number** (fig. 49). Outside of leaves blank, except for rectangular border on 1a.
Fixed string-gnomon dials; 1b half sun at top centre, 2a cardinal points in compass bowl offset, quatrefoil motif 11 thrice.

59. Probably Nuremberg, unsigned, c. 1500; found in the Thames. Leaf 1 missing. 67 × 46 × 8 mm; 20 mm. **210** (fig. 131).
2a horizontal dial; compass bowl blank, ring, needle and glass missing. Below a geometric pattern engraved.

60. Probably German, Nuremberg? Not later than 17th century; found in Town Ditch, London Wall. Ivory, cut transversely across the tusk, with brass attachments; red colouring. Diameter 72 mm; compass bowl diameter 22 mm. **ML A22451** (fig. 23).
1a dial for approximately 51°. Two of the numerals (VIII and IX) and the stars which indicate the half hours,

131 Lower leaf of ivory diptych, probably Nuremberg, c. 1500 Cat. 59.

have red colouring in them. The gnomon is missing, although the brass attachments are still in place at the centre and outer edge of the dial. The compass bowl is empty except for the brass ring which held the glass.
1b Decorated with engraving of tree with lopped-off branches. The milling marks of the tusk are clearly visible on this lower surface of the leaf, which is also badly cracked around the circumference. The dial has a turned ribbed basal edge.

61. German, probably Nuremberg, 16th century. Maker's mark of acorn. Found in Worship Street, London. Wood with brass fittings. Diameter 34 mm; compass bowl diameter 12 mm. **ML A3891** (fig. 132).
1a dial for a latitude of approximaely 51°. Compass bowl empty. The brass gnomon is embossed with the letters I R. Centre of the leaf decorated with two profiles – perhaps moon faces or human?
1b blank, except for the mark of an acorn incised on the leaf. (Part of a similar wooden dial, without provenance or accession number, which is kept with this identifiable instrument in the Museum of London, is also shown.)

132 Wooden compass dial, probably Nuremberg, 16th/17th century Cat. 61.

Select Bibliography

Manuscript Sources

Nürnberg Stadtarchiv (NSA)
  Behaim-Archiv no. 585
  Compaszmacher Schuldtbuch
  Libri Litt. (Grundverbriefungsbücher des
  Stadtgerichts, Rep. B. 14)
  Libri Cons.
  Inventarbücher des Stadtgerichts
  Rugamt Rep. B. 12, vols 138, 236

Nürnberg Staatsarchiv (NStA)
  Amts- u. Standbücher Rep. 52b, vol. 305, fols 186,
  187, 190, 196, 197
  Amts- u. Standbücher Rep. 52b, vol. 309, fol. 14
  Amts- u. Standbücher Rep. 52b, vols 259–261
  (versions of *Ordnung*)

Nürnberg Landeskirchliches Archiv (LKA)
  St. Lorenz Pfarre
    Taufbücher
    Taufregister
    Verkündbücher
    Verkündregister
    Totenbücher
  St. Sebald Pfarre
    Taufbücher
    Taufregister
    Verkündbücher
    Totenbücher

Printed Sources

Abbreviation:
MVGN = Mitteilungen des Vereins für Geschichte der Stadt Nürnberg

Africa Atlas
  J. F. Ade Ajayi and M. Crowder, *Historical Atlas of Africa* (London, 1985).

Agricola
  Georgius Agricola, *De re metallica libri XII*,
  translated from the first Latin edition of 1556 by
  H. C. Hoover and L. H. Hoover (London, 1912,
  reprint New York, 1950).

Archinard
  M. Archinard, 'A note on horizontal sundials',
  Bulletin of the Scientific Instrument Society, 14 (1987),
  6–7.

Balmer
  H. Balmer, *Beiträge zur Geschichte der Erkenntnis des Erdmagnetismus* (Aarau, 1956).

Barns
  T. A. Barns, *Tales of the Ivory Trade* (London, 1923).

Baron
  H. Baron, 'Religion and Politics in the German
  Imperial Cities during the Reformation', *English
  Historical Review*, 52 (1937), 405–27, 614–33.

Baxandall
  M. Baxandall, *The Limewood Sculptors of Renaissance
  Germany* (New Haven and London, 1980).

Bazin
  P. Bazin, *Les Ivoiriers dieppois au Museé de Dieppe*
  (Dieppe, 1972).

Belgian collections
  Société Generale de Banque, *La Mesure du temps dans
  les collections belges* (Brussels, 1984).

Berliner
  R. Berliner, *Ornamentale Vorlageblätter des 15. bis 19.
  Jahrhunderts,* 3 vols (Leipzig, 1925–26; new edn by
  G. Egger, Munich, 1981).

Bobinger
  M. Bobinger, *Alt-Augsburger Compassmacher*
  (Augsburg, 1966).

Bonelli
  M. L. Bonelli, *Catalogo degli strumenti del Museo di
  Storia della Scienza* (Florence, 1954).

Bovill
  E. E. Bovill, *The Golden Trade of the Moors* 2nd edn
  (London, 1968).

Braudel
  F. Braudel, *Civilization and Capitalism 15th–18th
  Centuries,* trans. S. Reynolds, 3 vols (London,
  1981–4); vol. 2 'The Wheels of Commerce.'

Brown & Kelly
  W. A. B. Brown and K. Kelly, 'The structure of
  elephant ivory', unpublished paper including results
  from using a new technique, the energy dispersive
  analysis of X-Rays (EDAX), 1987.

Bryden
  D. J. Bryden, *Whipple Museum of the History of Science,
  Catalogue 6: Sundials and Related Instruments*
  (Cambridge, 1988).

Burack

    B. Burack, *Ivory and its Uses* (Rutland, Vermont & Tokyo, 1984).

Byrne

    J. S. Byrne, *Renaissance Ornament Prints and Drawings* (New York, 1981).

CEH

    E. E. Rich and C. H. Wilson, eds, *The Cambridge Economic History of Europe,* vol. 4 (Cambridge, 1967).

Chandler & Vincent I

    B. Chandler and C. Vincent, 'A Sure Reckoning: Sundials of the 17th and 18th Centuries', *Metropolitan Museum of Art Bulletin,* 26 (1967), 154–69.

Chandler & Vincent II

    B. Chandler and C. Vincent, 'Three Nürnberg Compassmacher: Hans Troschel the Elder, Hans Troschel the Younger, and David Beringer', *Metropolitan Museum Journal,* 2 (1969), 211–16.

Cipolla

    C. Cipolla, ed., *Fontana Economic History of Europe,* vol. 2 'The Sixteenth and Seventeenth Centuries' (London, 1974).

Clair

    C. Clair, *A History of European Printing* (London, 1976).

Crawforth

    M. Crawforth, 'Diptych dials: cord characteristics', unpublished research paper, 1988.

Dettling

    K. Dettling, 'Der Metallhandel Nürnbergs im 16. Jahrhundert.', *MVGN,* 27 (1928), 99–241.

Doppelmayr

    Johann Gabriel Doppelmayr, *Historische Nachricht Von den Nürnbergischen Mathematicis und Künstlern* (Nuremberg, 1730).

Drecker

    J. Drecker, *Gnomon und Sonnenuhren* (Aachen, 1909).

DSB

    C. C. Gillispie, ed., *Dictionary of Scientific Biography,* 16 vols (New York, 1970–80).

Durand

    D. B. Durand, *The Vienna-Klosterneuburg Map Corpus* (Leiden, 1952).

Eisenstein

    E. L. Eisenstein, *The Printing Press as an Agent of Change* (paperback edn, Cambridge, 1980).

Endres

    R. Endres, 'Zur Einwohnerzahl und Bevölkerungsstuktur Nürnbergs im 15./16. Jahrhundert', *MVGN,* 57 (1970), 242–71.

J. Evans

    J. Evans, *Pattern: A Study of Ornament in Western Europe 1180–1900,* vol. 1 'The Middle Ages' (Oxford, 1931, Da Capo reprint New York, 1976).

L. Evans

    L. Evans, *Portable Sundials* (London, 1900).

Fleischmann

    P. Fleischmann, *Das Bauhandwerk in Nürnberg vom 14. bis zum 18. Jahrhundert* (Nuremberg, 1985).

Gallois

    L. Gallois, *Les Géographes allemands de la Renaissance* (Paris, 1890, reprint Amsterdam, 1963).

Gettens & Stout

    R. J. Gettens and G. L. Stout, *Painting Materials* (New York, 1942, reprint 1946).

Gouk

    P. M. Gouk, 'The union of arts and sciences in the eighteenth century: Lorenz Spengler (1720–1807), artistic turner and natural scientist', *Annals of Science,* 40 (1983), 411–36.

Gümbel

    A. Gümbel, 'Das Inventar der Scherlschen Kunstkammer in Nürnberg vom Jahre 1637', *MVGN,* 30 (1931), 321–37.

Hampe

    T. Hampe, *Die Nürnberger Ratsverlässe über Kunst und Künstler im Zeitalter der Spätgotik und Renaissance 1449–1618,* 3 vols (Vienna, 1904).

Hartmann

    J. Hartmann, *Die astronomischen Instrumente des Kardinals Nikolaus Cusanus* (Berlin, 1919).

Harley

    R. D. Harley, *Artists' Pigments c. 1600–1835: A Study in English Documentary Sources* (London, 1970).

Hayward

    J. F. Hayward, *Virtuoso Goldsmiths and the Triumph of Mannerism, 1540–1620* (London, 1976).

Henderson, Mortimer & Hackmann

    J. Henderson, C. Mortimer and W. D. Hackmann, 'Analysis of diptych dials', unpublished report of analysis undertaken for the Museum of the History of Science, Oxford, at the Research Laboratory for Archaeology and the History of Art, Oxford, 1988.

Henkel & Schöne

    A. Henkel and A. Schöne, eds, *Emblemata. Handbuch zur Sinnbildkunst des XVI. und XVII. Jahrhunderts* (Stuttgart, 1967).

Higgins I

    K. Higgins, 'The classification of sundials', *Annals of Science,* 9 (1953), 342–58.

Higgins II

    K. Higgins, 'The development of the sundial between A.D. 1400 and 1800' (1953), unpublished B.Sc. thesis, Oxford, Museum of the History of Science, Oxford, MS Museum 224.

Hind

A. M. Hind, *A History of Engraving and Etching from the 15th century to 1914* (London, 1923, 2nd impression 1927).

History of Technology

C. Singer, E. J. Holmyard, A. R. Hall, and T. I. Williams, eds, *A History of Technology,* 8 vols (Oxford, 1954–1984).

Hodges

H. Hodges, *Artifacts: An Introduction to Early Materials and Technology* (London, 1964).

Holtzapffel

C. Holtzapffel, *Turning and Mechanical Manipulation* 5 vols (London, 1846–1884).

Hyatt

A. H. Hyatt, *A Book of Sundial Mottoes* (New York, 1903).

Irmscher

G. Irmscher, 'Der Nürnberger Ornamentstich im 16. u. 17. Jahrhundert', in *Wenzel Jamnitzer und die Nürnberger Goldschmiedekunst 1500–1700: Eine Ausstellung im Germanischen Nationalmuseum Nürnberg vom 28. Juni–15. September 1985* (Munich, 1985), 141–50.

Jegel

A. Jegel, *Alt-Nürnberger Handwerksrecht und seine Beziehungen zu andern* (Neustadt an der Aisch, 1965).

Josten

C. H. Josten, *A Catalogue of Scientific Instruments. From the 13th to the 19th Centuries. From the Collection of J. A. Billmeir, C.B.E.* (2nd edn, Oxford, 1955).

Kellenbenz I

H. Kellenbenz, *Das Meder'sche Handelsbuch und die Welser'schen Nachträge* (Wiesbaden 1974).

Kellenbenz II

H. Kellenbenz, *The Rise of the European Economy 1500–1700* (London, 1976).

Körber

H. G. Körber, *Zur Geschichte der Konstruktion von Sonnenuhren und Kompassen des 16. bis 18. Jahrhunderts.* (Berlin, 1965).

Kühnlein

H. Kühnlein, 'Die Kompassmacherfamilie Tucher in Nürnberg und ihr Handwerk', *Blätter für Fränkische Familienkunde,* 12 (1986), 318–25.

Landes

D. S. Landes, *Revolution in Time: Clocks and the Making of the Modern World* (Cambridge, Ma., and London, 1983).

Lockner

H. P. Lockner, *Die Merkzeichen der Nürnberger Rotschmiede* (Munich, 1981).

Longhurst

M. Longhurst, *Catalogue of Carvings in Ivory in the Victoria and Albert Museum,* 2 vols (London, 1927–9).

MacGregor

A. MacGregor, *Bone, Antler, Ivory and Horn: The Technology of Skeletal Materials since the Roman Period* (London, 1985).

Maddison

F. R. Maddison, *A Supplement to a Catalogue of Scientific Instruments. In the Collection of J. A. Billmeir, Esq., C.B.E. Exhibited by the Museum of the History of Science, Oxford* (Oxford and London, 1957).

Marque

A. H. de Oliveira Marque, *History of Portugal* (2nd edn, New York, 1976).

Maskell

A. Maskell, *Ivories* (London, 1905).

Maurice

K. Maurice, *Sovereigns as Turners: Materials on a Machine Art by Princes,* trans. D. A. Schade (Zürich, 1985).

Mayall & Mayall

R. N. Mayall and M. L. Mayall, *Sundials: How to Know, Use, and Make Them* (Boston, 1938).

Melot

M. Melot *et al., Prints* (London, 1981).

Michel I

H. Michel, *Les Cadrans solaires de Max Elskamp* (Liège, 1966).

Michel II

H. Michel, *Scientific Instruments in Art and History,* trans. R. E. W. and F. R. Maddison (London, 1967).

Milan

Musei e Gallerie di Milano, *Museo Poldi-Pezzoli: Orologi-Oreficerie* (Milan, 1981), 19–21, plates pp. 40–55.

Milet

A. Milet, *Ivoires et Ivoiriers de Dieppe* (Paris, 1906).

Moxon

Joseph Moxon, *Mechanick Exercises* (3rd edn London, 1703, reprint London and New York, 1970).

Murdoch

T. Murdoch, 'Some Huguenot craftsmen from Dieppe in London', *17th Century French Studies,* 6 (1984), 60–74.

Müller

J. Müller, 'Der Umfang und die Hauptrouten des Nürnberger Handelsgebietes im Mittelalter', *Vierteljahresschrift für Sozial- und Wirtschaftsgeschichte,* 6 (1908), 1–38.

de Murr

Christophe Theophile de Murr, *Description du Cabinet de Monsieur Paul de Praun à Nuremberg* (Nuremberg, 1797).

O'Dell-Franke

I. O'Dell-Franke, *Kupferstiche und Radierungen aus der Werkstatt des Virgil Solis* (Wiesbaden, 1977).

Parry

J. H. Parry, *The Age of Reconnaissance 1450–1650* (London, 1963).

Pfeiffer

G. Pfeiffer, ed., *Nürnberg: Geschichte einer europäischen Stadt* (Munich, 1971).

Philippovich I

E. von Philippovich, 'Elfenbeinkunstwerke Nürnberger Provenienz' *MVGN*, 49 (1959), 319–60.

Philippovich II

E. von Philippovich, *Elfenbein*, 2nd edn (Brunswick, 1961).

Pilz I

K. Pilz, *Das Handwerk in Nürnberg und in Mittelfranken* (Nuremberg, 1954).

Pilz II

K. Pilz, *600 Jahre Astronomie in Nürnberg* (Nuremberg, 1977).

Pirckheimer

Willibald Pirckheimer, *Geographia Claudii Ptolemaei* (Basle, 1545).

Regiomontan

Johannes Regiomontan, *Der deutsche Kalender des Johannes Regiomontan. Nürnberg, um 1474,* facsimile edn, with an introduction by E. Zinner (Leipzig, 1937).

Ritchie

C. I. A. Ritchie, *Ivory Carving* (London, 1969).

Roach

W. Roach, 'William Smith: A Description of the Cittie of Noremberg (Beschreibung der Reichsstadt Nürnberg) 1594', *MVGN*, 48 (1958), 194–245.

Rohde

A. Rohde, *Die Geschichte der wissenschaftlichen Instrumente vom Beginn der Renaissance bis zum Ausgang des 18. Jahrhunderts* (Leipzig, 1923).

Rohr

R. R. J. Rohr, *Sundials. History, Theory and Practice* (Toronto and Buffalo, 1970).

Russell

K. F. Russell, 'Ivory anatomical manikins', *Medical History,* 16 (1972), 131–42.

Schaefer

K. Schaefer, 'Des Hieronymus Braun Prospekt der Stadt Nürnberg vom Jahre 1608 und Seine Vorläufer', *MVGN,* 12 (1896), 3–84.

Schnelbögl I

F. Schnelbögl, 'Life and Work of the Nuremberg Cartographer Erhard Etzlaub (+1532)', *Imago Mundi* 20 (1966), 11–26.

Schnelbögl II

F. Schnelbögl, 'Leben und Werk des Nürnberger Kartographen Erhard Etzlaub (+1532)', *MVGN,* 57 (1970), 216–31.

Schroeder

W. Schroeder, *Practical Astronomy* (London, 1956).

Seebass

G. Seebass, 'The Reformation in Nürnberg', in *The Social History of the Reformation,* ed. L. P. Buck and J. W. Zophy (Columbia, 1972), 17–40.

Smith

J. C. Smith, ed., *Nuremberg, A Renaissance City, 1500–1618* (Austin, Texas, 1983).

Stockbauer

J. Stockbauer, *Nürnbergisches Handwerksrecht des XVI Jahrhunderts* (Nuremberg, 1879).

Stöfler

Johannes Stöfler, *Elucidatio fabricae ususque astrolabii* (Oppenheim, 1524).

Strauss

G. Strauss, *Nuremberg in the Sixteenth Century* (New York and London, 1966).

Taylor I

E. G. R. Taylor, 'Early charts and the origin of the compass rose', *Jl. Institute of Navigation,* 4 (1951), 351–6.

Taylor II

E. G. R. Taylor, 'The south-pointing needle', *Imago Mundi,* 8 (1961), 1–7.

Theophilus

J. G. Hawthorne and C. S. Smith, eds, *On Divers Arts: The Treatise of Theophilus* (Chicago, 1963).

Turner

A. J. Turner, *Early Scientific Instruments: Europe 1400–1800* (London, 1987).

Vincent & Chandler

C. Vincent and B. Chandler, 'Night-time and Easter Time: The Rotations of the Sun, the Moon, and the Little Bear in Renaissance Time Reckoning', *Metropolitan Museum of Art Bulletin,* 2 (1969), 372–84.

H. Wagner

H. Wagner, 'P. Apians Bestimmung der magnetischen Missweisung von 1532 und die Nürnberger Compassmacher', *Nachrichten d. Ges. d. Wiss. Göttingen, Phil. Hist. Kl.* (1901), 179–82.

M. Wagner I

M. Wagner, *Nürnberger Handwerker. Bilder und Aufzeichnungen aus den Zwölfbrüderhäusern 1388–1807* (Wiesbaden, 1987).

M. Wagner II

M. Wagner, *Das alte Nürnberg. Einblick in vier Jahrhunderte Handwerksleben* (Hürtgenwald, 1980).

Ward

F. A. B. Ward, *A Catalogue of European Scientific Instruments in the Department of Medieval and Later Antiquities of the British Museum* (London, 1981).

Waters

D. Waters, *The Art of Navigation in England in Elizabethan and Early Stuart Times* (London, 1958).

Waugh

A. Waugh, *Sundials: Their Theory and Construction* (New York, 1973).

Werner

T. G. Werner, 'Nürnbergs Erzeugung und Ausfuhr wissenschaftlicher Geräte im Zeitalter der Entdeckungen', *MVGN,* 53 (1965), 69–149.

G. Williamson

G. C. Williamson, *The Book of Ivory* (London, 1938).

P. Williamson

P. Williamson, *An Introduction to Medieval Ivory Carvings* (London, 1982).

Wilson & Ayerst

D. Wilson and P. Ayerst, *White Gold: The Story of African Ivory* (London, 1976).

Winter

J. Winter, 'The characterization of pigments based on carbon', *Studies in Conservation,* 28 (1983), 49–66.

Woodbury

R. S. Woodbury, *History of the Lathe to 1850* (Cambridge, Ma., 1961).

Wörthmüller

W. Wörthmüller, 'Die Nürnberger Trompeten- und Posauenmacher des 17. und 18. Jahrhunderts', *MVGN,* 45 (1954), 208–325, 372–480.

Wynter & Turner

H. Wynter and A. Turner, *Scientific Instruments* (London, 1975).

Zinner I

E. Zinner, *Deutsch und niederländische astronomische Instrumente des 11–18 Jahrhunderts* (revised edn, Munich, 1967; reprint 1979).

Zinner II

E. Zinner, 'Nürnbergs wissenschaftliche Bedeutung am Ende des Mittelalters', *MVGN,* 50 (1960), 113–19.

Zinner III

E. Zinner, *Leben und Wirken des Joh. Müller von Königsberg genannt Regiomontanus,* 2nd edn (Osnabrück, 1968).

Index